sex
FOR EVERYONE

By the same Author

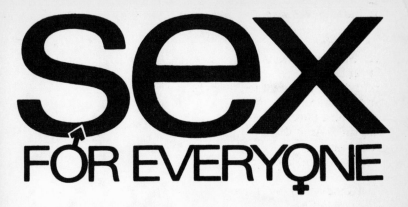

sex
FOR EVERYONE

HOW TO HAVE FUN WITHOUT FEAR

DR VERNON COLEMAN

ANGUS
& ROBERTSON
PUBLISHERS

Dedicated to X

The chromosome that makes the difference

ANGUS & ROBERTSON PUBLISHERS

16 Golden Square, London W1R 4BN,
United Kingdom and
Unit 4, Eden Park, 31 Waterloo Road,
North Ryde, NSW, Australia 2113.

First published in the United Kingdom by
Angus & Robertson (UK) in 1989

Typeset in Great Britain by
The Word Shop, Rossendale, Lancs.

Printed in Finland

British Library Cataloguing in Publication Data

    Coleman, Dr Vernon
    Sex for everyone.
    1. Man. Sexual & intercourse
    I. Title
    612'.6

ISBN 0 207 16430 4

Contents

Foreword

For most of the 1980s sex was overshadowed by AIDS. The emphasis was on safety and caution. Doctors, politicians and journalists combined to take the fun out of sex and replace it with fear.

It is now clear that the threat of AIDS to heterosexuals was wildly and irresponsibly exaggerated. AIDS is a major danger to homosexuals and to drug addicts but not to men who love women or women who love men. The truth is that AIDS is no more a sexually transmitted disease than influenza or tuberculosis.

I've kept two aims in mind while writing this book. First, to get rid of all the myths and misunderstandings about sex; to deal honestly and carefully with fears, anxieties and apprehensions. Consequently much of this book is very serious. When sexual problems develop they *need* to be treated seriously. But my approach isn't entirely earnest. I've tried to add a lighthearted touch here and there. After all, sex is supposed to be pleasureable! So my second aim has been to put the *fun* back into sex, to entertain as well as to provide reassurance and information.

Vernon Coleman
Devon 1989

Chapter 1

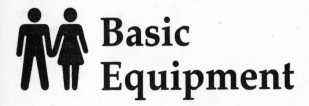 Basic Equipment

Please bear with me if this chapter seems a bit dull. The trouble with anatomy is that even when it involves the most interesting bits of the human body it is still fairly tedious. If you feel you already know everything you want to know about your body (and your partner's) then please feel free to skip the next few pages. Later on, if you come across things you don't understand, you can always pop back to this introductory section. If, on the other hand, you'd like to know how an erection develops, what happens when someone has an orgasm and how fast semen travels when it leaves the penis, do read on.

Basic Equipment – Her

The external, visible, sexual parts of a woman are collectively known as the vulva. At the upper end of the vulva is an area usually covered in a fairly luxurious growth of tightly curled pubic hair. This area is known as the *mons veneris* or Mount of Venus (named, most appropriately after the Roman goddess of love). The *mons* is made of a pad of fat that covers the hard pubic bone and acts as a cushion during intercourse.

Below the *mons veneris* the two outermost parts of the vulva are the *labia majora*, the outer lips of the vagina, which are also normally covered with pubic hair. They are made of elongated rolls of fat and embryologists regard them as the female equivalent of the male scrotum. It is a fact of life but of little consequence that the left *labia majora* is usually slightly larger than the right.

Inside these two large, outer lips are the rather smaller, inner *labia minora*. These two delicate folds of skin are usually free from pubic hair and they run parallel to the outer lips. Again, the left and right *labia minora* are quite commonly of different sizes, and also vary from person to person. In some parts of the world a large pair of *labia minora* are considered to be the essence of real beauty. Their colour varies too and tends to change from a pale pink to a rich, dark purple when their owner is sexually excited.

The gap between the two *labia minora* is known as the vestibule – aptly named since it is the entrance to the vagina – and above the vestibule the two small, inner lips meet just underneath the *mons veneris*. A small distance before they meet the two inner lips both split into two forming a small protective hood for the clitoris. Normally the *labia minora* are closed together to seal off the vagina from the outside world.

Inch for inch the clitoris is one of the most powerful and influential organs in the female body. It is the female equivalent of the male penis and contains the same sort of erectile tissue that fills with blood and swells during sexual excitement. Like the uncircumcised penis the clitoris is covered with a foreskin. Its size and shape varies enormously from one woman to another but when unstimulated it is usually about the size of a pea. The clitoris is exquisitely tender to the touch since it contains many nerve endings. Its sole function seems to be to provide sexual pleasure.

In some women the clitoris is stimulated naturally during intercourse. When the *labia minora* are pulled by the penis moving in and out of the vagina the clitoris is gently massaged by the movement. Remember the two inner lips both split and surround the clitoris. Sometimes, however, the clitoris needs to be stimulated directly before it responds appropriately. Sometimes women say their clitoris is so sensitive that direct stimulation is unbearable. When stimulated properly the clitoris gets bigger and harder.

Still at the top end of the vestibule, and just below the clitoris, is the urethra, the opening which connects the bladder to the outside world. Strong sphincter muscles which are able to close together tightly normally ensure that urine only flows out of the bladder when the moment is appropriate but sometimes these

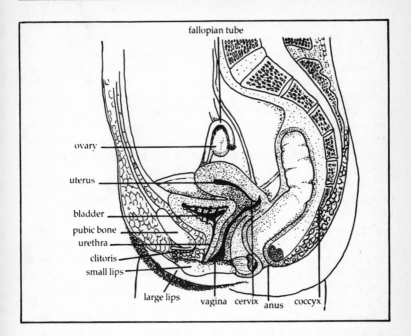

muscles relax a little when a woman is sexually aroused. When this happens a little urine may leak out. This really doesn't matter. It certainly does no harm. Indeed, it simply adds to the lubrication which makes intercourse more pleasurable for both partners. However, if desired, leakage of urine during sex can usually be avoided by emptying the bladder before sex.

Directly below the urethra is the vagina, a rather larger opening leading to a muscular tube which stretches back and up towards the womb or uterus. In young girls the opening of the vagina is often partly (and sometimes completely) sealed by the hymen, a thin sheet of skin across the mouth of the vagina. The hymen usually dissolves and disappears as the girl grows and develops, leaving remnants around the vaginal entrance.

In what are sweetly called 'the olden days' the existence of a hymen used to be regarded as evidence that a girl was still a virgin, and a groom would expect his bride to suffer some pain as he first stretched and then split her hymen. A few spots of blood on the bridal sheet were expected and their absence could lead to vicious accusations. In some societies it is still considered an insult to the husband if a new wife doesn't bleed when the marriage is consummated. These days, however, particularly in the West, most brides, whether virginal or not, have little or no hymen left by their wedding night. The membrane is often split by horse or bicycle riding, gymnastics or the use of tampons during menstruation. Sometimes, however, the hymen can be very thick and may need to be surgically pierced if consummation of the marriage or relationship is not possible.

Before I go on to describe the vagina it is, I think, worth pointing out that it is important not to confuse the vaginal opening with the urethra above it. If the urethra is mistakenly used in lieu of the vagina incontinence and apparent infertility are almost inevitable consequences. Such a mistake may seem unlikely to the experienced but it is more common than people would imagine.

The first third of the vagina is made up of a strong ring of muscles which enable the vagina to remain closed when not in use and which give it the ability to grasp anything that happens to be inside it quite tightly. When these muscles are exercised they can be remarkably strong. (There is a description of suitable exercises on page 152). Night-club entertainers sometimes develop their vaginal musculature to such an extent that they can perform remarkable tricks with cigarettes, table-tennis balls and other objects. More usefully, the vaginal muscles can be developed to improve the woman's sexual skills.

The size of a vagina is a subject of concern to both men and women. In certain African and Asian tribes a man looking to buy a new wife will examine her first to check out the size and depth of her vagina and make sure that it will be suitable. He will also check how thick her *labia* are and how well padded her *mons veneris* is.

Some women, from all sorts of cultures, particularly young and innocent women, worry that their vaginas will be too small to accommodate an erect penis. Other women, who may be older and more experienced and have had one or two children, worry that their vaginas may have become too spacious. These fears and concerns are needless. The size of a woman's vagina has little or no effect on the pleasure she or her partner may obtain. The vagina can stretch to accommodate a baby's head – which is much larger than any penis ever reported – while the muscles within the vaginal walls enable a woman to hold tightly onto a penis of quite modest proportions. If a woman is unusually tiny and her partner has a penis of exceptional proportions, the only real risk is that by penetrating too far and too energetically he may knock an ovary with the end of his penis. Ovaries, like testicles, are well endowed with nerve endings and this can be exceedingly painful.

Inside the vagina, the muscular walls are covered with a membrane which contains remarkably few nerve endings. The vagina has three functions: to let the penis in, to allow a baby out and to provide an avenue through which the monthly menstrual flow can escape. It is remarkably well adapted to these functions.

Just inside the vaginal opening there are two small glands, one on each side, which secrete fluid during sexual excitement and moisten the vaginal entrance making it easier for the penis to enter. These are known as Bartholin's glands and occasionally they can become infected and swollen. In addition to these secretions the walls of the vagina also produce something called lactic acid. This helps to kill off any bugs which might get inside an area that, being warm and moist, would otherwise be an excellent breeding ground for infections of all kinds. The production of these secretions of lactic acid increases during a woman's reproductive years so that any risk of infection is kept to a minimum during the time when pregnancy might ensue. Before puberty and after the menopause the production of secretions drops away and soreness, dryness and infection are more common. Incidentally, the amount of moisture inside the vagina is not only dependent on sexual excitement. The vagina can also be made more moist by happiness, fear and nervousness. There is a slight increase in the amount of vaginal secretion before a menstrual period and a reduction during menstruation (so that sex during a period can be dry and painful). During sex itself the vagina produces more secretions, equivalent in quantity to a male ejaculation.

Infection is the only other factor likely to increase the amount of fluid secreted by the vagina. The smell and colour of a discharge produced by an infection usually makes the problem unmistakable.

The clitoris is universally accepted as the main stimulus for sexual excitement in a woman, but it has some competition. According to some researchers there is a bean shaped patch of erectile tissue attached to the inside of the top part of the vagina and situated about 1 to 2 inches (2.5 to 5cms) inside it. This area, said to be directly behind the pubic bone, is alleged to be 1 to 1½ inches (2.5 to 4cms) across and is known as the G-spot after its discoverer, Ernst Grafenberg.

Grafenberg was a German gynaecologist. He discovered the G-spot in the 1940s when he was researching different methods of birth control, and claimed that when stimulated by pressure the G-spot triggered a vaginal orgasm. His claims substantiated the earlier, controversial claims that women can have two quite different types of orgasm – those inspired by stimulation of the clitoris and those triggered by movement inside the vagina. I'll deal with this controversy later on when I deal with the orgasm (see page 25).

Apart from producing an orgasm, stimulation of the G-spot is also alleged to produce fluid. Three American researchers have claimed that the G-spot is a sort of female prostate gland and it has been argued that the spot, patch of tissue, gland or whatever it is secretes a special fluid during orgasm, a claim which has given rise to the suggestion that women may really ejaculate when they reach a climax. Some researchers claim that the fluid produced by the G-spot emerges from the urethra and explain this phenomenon by pointing out that the G-spot extends from the top part of the vagina to the lower part of the urethra.

Despite these claims there is still a good deal of confusion about whether or not the G-spot really exists, how it works if it does exist and precisely what its function is. Gynaecologists who still haven't identified the spot claim that to look for it would be distinctly unethical and professionally hazardous since, if they found it, their patients might get the wrong idea. Pathologists, who claim that they haven't been able to find the bean-shaped patch when dissecting cadavers in the post mortem room, have been told that the G-spot atrophies in older women. Some sexperts claim that it is possible that the G-spot only exists in some women and that only a few women genuinely ejaculate. Others have dismissed the whole idea as nonsense and argued that the controversy causes much un-necessary anxiety, and many feelings of inadequacy, among both women and men. I am, I confess, a supporter of this last group. The existence or absence of the G-spot is, it seems to me, more a question for philosophers than physiologists. Sexperts should concentrate more on satisfying their patients needs than their own curiosity.

Inside and at the top end of the vagina can be felt the cervix or neck of the womb. The womb, also known as the uterus, is hollow and shaped like an upsidedown pear with the stalk pulled out. The narrow end of the pear-shaped womb is the cervix. The uterus consists of extremely powerful muscles which can stretch to many times their normal size for months at a time when a woman is pregnant. The lining of the womb, the endometrium, is controlled by hormones and the bleeding which marks the end of each menstrual cycle is a result of the endometrium breaking down and being discharged from the uterus.

The womb lining develops each month to provide a nourishing site for any egg which may be fertilized, giving it the chance to mature into a foetus. Since the womb is tucked away within a woman's body any developing baby will be well protected from the world outside by thick muscle and hard bone.

Eggs, produced from the ovaries, get into the womb by travelling along one of the two Fallopian tubes which provide a connecting passageway between the ovaries and the upper part of the uterus. The ovaries are the female equivalent of the male testicles; they manufacture the female sex hormones oestrogen and progesterone and store a supply of approximately half a million immature eggs. Roughly every twenty-eight days an egg matures and leaves the ovary ready for conception. Astonishingly less than 0.1 per cent of the available eggs will ever reach the uterus; the rest are 'spares'.

If sperm manage to get through the cervix and into the uterus at roughly the same time as an egg is released then the two may get together. The sperm will fertilize the egg and a baby will start to grow. If no egg gets fertilized, the endometrium – the special lining in the uterus that develops to support a foetus – isn't needed and is discharged as a monthly bleed ready for the whole cycle to begin again.

👫 Basic Equipment – Him

Unlike a woman, whose sexual apparatus is largely hidden both from her and from any casual observer, a man's reproductive equipment is highly visible. It consists of a penis and a scrotum in which two testicles are stored.

The male role in sex is quite simple. A man is designed to do two things: to produce sperm and to deposit those sperm as close to a woman's womb as possible. To give a good chance of fertilization, sperm needs to enter the womb in large numbers, and yet the neck of the womb is, for a tiny sperm at least, quite a long way inside a woman's body. If sperm were deposited at the entrance to the vagina they'd never make the journey; it would be like dumping children twenty miles from the school gates and expecting them to walk. To get over this problem the penis is designed to deposit sperm remarkably close to the target.

In order to penetrate the soft-walled vagina the penis has to get hard. There is some evidence that many thousands of years ago the penis may have included a bone to make penetration easy, and in France just thirty years ago X-ray evidence was obtained of a male with a small bone built into his penis. But a bone is, obviously, impractical and man evolved with a boneless penis. Nature decided long ago to economize with male architecture so in addition to serving a vital role as a sex organ the penis also functions as a discharge route for urine. The opening at the end of the penis, in the centre of the glans, emits both urine and semen, but a valve ensures that the penis is only used to urinate when it is limp; a man cannot urinate with an erection.

By using the same route for semen and urine there is a very modest saving in male design – although it wouldn't have been difficult to put the urethral opening just below the penis. It is difficult to imagine that man's development would have been put back by not being able to pass urine standing up.

Having the penis do two jobs is actually something of a design fault because it can, and does, lead to all sorts of problems. For example, during sexual intercourse the opening of the urethra at the tip of the penis comes into direct contact with the inside of the vagina. If the vagina is infected then this can cause an infection and inflammation of the male urethra. In women the urethra remains unobtrusive and has relatively little exposure to infection although there is a snag with having a short urethra – bugs can reach the bladder more easily. This means that women are more susceptible to bladder infections than men while men are more susceptible to urethra infections than women. The other problem produced by this twin function is that if the prostate gland, which supplies part of the seminal fluid, enlarges (as it sometimes does in old age) the urethra can be squeezed and closed causing urine retention.

In its normal state the male penis is quite limp and flaccid. It is well designed for urination but would be quite unable to penetrate the vagina. Try threading a needle with a limp and dangling end of cotton. The hardening and erection is made possible by the existence within it of columns of spongy tissue which fill with blood when a man is sexually excited. When the erect penis then rubs against the inside of the vagina the stimulation triggers an ejaculatory mechanism which fires sperm towards the womb. When perfectly positioned the end of the penis touches the cervix and sperm are fired directly into the womb, greatly increasing the chances of the recipient becoming pregnant.

But I'm getting a little ahead of myself. Before I go on to describe the mechanisms which result in sperm being fired towards the womb I need to describe the penis itself in a little more detail. I'll begin with some basic statistics.

At birth the average erect penis is little more than 1 inch (2.5cms) long. By the age of twelve it is double that length. By the age of fifteen the average penis is nearly 5 inches (12.5cms) long and by seventeen slightly over. The height and weight of the owner bear little relationship to the size of a penis and it really isn't true that you can tell the size of a man's penis by looking at his feet or his nose. The penis does, however, tend to get slightly larger with age – one of the few physical benefits associated with ageing. The length of a fairly ordinary, inconspicuous sort of penis can increase by as much as an inch throughout its lifetime. Finally, there are slight racial differences: orientals tend to have slightly smaller penises than caucasians and negroes tend to have slightly larger ones.

By full adulthood the average erect penis is over 6½ inches (nearly 17cms) long and 3½ inches (9cms) in circumference. (It sounds much more impressive in metric terms!) The majority of men are remarkably close to this average and genuine, appreciable, noticeable underdevelopment is rare and usually accompanied by other signs of poor development.

Numerous devices and creams are sold to help enlarge a penis that the owner thinks is too small but none of them really work and some are harmful. For example, some 'vacuum' devices designed to draw blood into the penis can rupture blood vessels and make it harder for the unfortunate male to acquire a decent erection. The only thing that does increase penis size is, it seems, sexual intercourse. Some experts claim that if a man has sex often then his penis will grow slightly larger.

The size of the average penis seems to have got slightly bigger over the last century or so. Surveys done in the late nineteenth century showed that the length of the average penis ranged from nearly 3 inches to 4½ inches (nearly 7.5 to 1.5cms). It's difficult to explain this difference. Maybe measuring techniques have changed over the years.

Incidentally, any man who wants to compare the length of his penis with the average I've quoted above should grasp the end of his penis (gently!) between thumb and first finger and stretch it as far as possible along a ruler which has one end pushed firmly against his pubic bone. It's best not to allow a companion to hold the ruler (or the penis) since this can produce a distorted figure. I should perhaps point out that it is the length to the tip of the glans of the penis that should be measured, not the length to the end of a stretched foreskin! The penis should be measured while erect.

Men worry a lot about the size of their organ. Young boys often feel underendowed when they look around in the school showers. What they do not realize is that boys of a similar age may have reached puberty earlier and their organs may, therefore, have started to get larger. Remember the size of the average penis more than doubles between the ages of twelve and fifteen. Boys also fail to realize that the size of their own penis is 'shortened' when they look down on it. If two males face one another naked both will almost always think that the other has a larger penis.

The worries continue into adulthood.

Some men worry that their penises may be too large and they may hurt the women they make love to. This is possible though it is a rare problem since the female vagina can, as I have already explained, expand and adapt itself to cope with a baby's head. No one in history has had a penis as thick as a baby's head. The only real hazard is that if a penis is unusually long it may deposit sperm in the vaginal cul de sac behind the cervix. This means that it is difficult for sperm to get into the womb and so the woman may have difficulty in getting pregnant. In addition, a penis that is too long may prevent a woman reaching an orgasm by painfully lifting her uterus upwards. On the other hand, a penis that is just long enough to hit the cervix may trigger an orgasm as it does so. Finally, an unusually large penis will need to become very hard in order to force its way between the *labia minora* into the vagina. A man with a very large penis will not be able to get away with a half-hearted erection.

It is much more common for men to worry that their penis is too small than too big and this widespread concern about penis size is not confined to heterosexual males. A study of 1000 gay men in America showed that 37 per cent thought that the size of a partner's penis was very important. Almost all homosexuals interviewed – even those with organs that were 8 inches (20cms) or more long – felt their penises were too small. A similar fear is common to males of other species. Among some monkeys the one with the longest penis is automatically made boss while the size of a baboon's penis plays a part in his acceptance, or otherwise, by the local females. A poorly endowed baboon may find himself wandering off into the jungle with his tail between his legs.

The truth, however, is that no consistent relationship exists between the size of a man's penis and his ability to satisfy a woman sexually. When women do find large penises exciting it is usually because they *look* more stimulating and because they are more fun to touch and play with rather than because they provide more direct sexual satisfaction.

I can't leave the subject of penis size without pointing out that although undersized penises are rare there are some men who have unusually small organs. About one in a thousand men have small penises because of a chromosomal abnormality known as Klinefelter's Syndrome. Instead of having one X and one Y chromosome (the normal male complement) patients with this problem have two X chromosomes and one Y chromosome. The extra female chromosome means that such patients have female breasts, tend to be obese and have a low sperm count. They show very little interest in sex. Even rarer is a condition known as micro penis in which the male organ is so small that the victims are sometimes reared as girls. Medical treatment with hormones may help although doctors and patients have to decide whether the child is treated as a girl or a boy before this can be started.

So far I have dealt only with the size of the erect penis. There is, of course, an appreciable change in size when a penis becomes erect. One significant effect erection has is that the penis size tends to even out: a penis that seems particularly small when limp may double or more than double its length

when erect whereas the increase in length of a larger penis will
be less marked. The length and width of a penis at rest gives no
indication of its potential when aroused; in some men the
thickness increases more than anything else, in others the main
effect of erection is to increase the length.

In one memorable scientific experiment a number of erect
penises were placed in containers of warm water (I still haven't
worked out how they did this – think about it) and the observers
noted that on average the erect penis has between three and
seven times the volume of a flaccid penis. Relatively few
experiments like this have been performed. Researchers pre-
sumably find it difficult to obtain volunteers prepared to waste a
perfectly good erection on a container of water. But the available
evidence does confirm that flaccid size bears no relationship to
the size of a penis when erect. A penis which is small and
unremarkable when limp may, when erect, become larger than
a penis which promises more when limp. Nature it seems, has
her own way of distributing her favours evenly.

Before I leave the subject of penis size it is perhaps worth
pointing out that the thickness of a penis has far more effect on a
woman's chances of reaching an orgasm than its length. The
unstretched vagina is only about 4 to 5 inches (10 to 12.5cms)
long so the average erect penis is too long to be inserted to its
base, and does not need to be. However, the thicker a penis is
the more likely it is to stretch the *labia minora* as it moves in and
out. It is the movement of the *labia minora* which stimulates the
clitoris and produces the female orgasm.

So much for size.

Whatever its length, the physical design of one penis is much
the same as any other. At birth the penis consists of two clearly
defined parts – the shaft and, at the end, the sensitive glans
which is partly or, frequently, completely covered by the
foreskin, a loose extension of the skin covering the rest of the
penis. Underneath the penis a fold of skin, the *frenulum*, binds
the glans to the body of the penis. If this is too short it will
prevent the penis erecting properly and will lead to premature
ejaculation. In 96 per cent of all male babies the foreskin is so
tight that it cannot be drawn back from the glans. By the time a
boy reaches puberty his foreskin is usually much looser. When
male hormones circulate at puberty the glans pushes out
through the foreskin.

For a variety of reasons (described on page 170) the foreskin is sometimes removed but it is vital to remember that this apparently useless piece of skin exists to protect the glans from external irritants. In men who have no foreskin the urethra gets smaller and smaller with gradual but continual scarring. There is also some evidence that without a foreskin the glans becomes slightly less sensitive. On the inner surface of the double fold produced by the foreskin are many small glands which produce a type of lubricating grease

The mechanisms which enable a penis to become erect function more or less from birth. Babies just a day or two old sometimes have erections. Just before puberty the ability of the penis to become erect increases sharply and boys of nine and ten can have erections perfectly capable of penetrating a vagina. It is clear they are created by a reflex reaction.

Babies' erections are the result of the automatic erectile reflex being triggered – the cause is a mystery. A few Eastern yogi can produce an erection by deliberate thought but for most men the erection is not under voluntary control – it either comes or it doesn't. Some sort of sexual stimulus is the usual reason, and the reflex is reinforced by regular activity. A man who has sex a lot will probably find it easier to get an erection when he wants to make love than a man who has sex only very rarely. Impotence can develop from disuse.

What happens during an erection is that muscle fibres inside the penis become relaxed and loosened so that blood can flow into and through the arteries inside the penis. Normally when the penis is limp these arteries are kept closed. When the arteries are opened blood rushes through them to fill the cavities of the spongy tissue inside the penis. This inflow of blood compresses the veins through which the blood would normally return so that the penis gradually gets larger and larger. The penis rises into an upright position during erection because there is more of the spongy, erectile tissue on its lower side. When this tissue fills with blood and expands it forces the whole penis upwards so that it is in a more appropriate position for penetration of the vagina.

In some animals – bulls, for example – an erection develops quite automatically when a female in heat is approached. It is, I suppose, fair to say that this is true of some men and, maybe of many men in some circumstances. During the Second World War large numbers of men stood in line to relieve themselves within whores whom they had never seen before. Each sexual event was over in an instant with no preparation, no foreplay and no opportunity for romance. It is easy to draw an analogy between the servicing of a cow by a bull and the relief of male frustration by the instantaneous penetration of a willing woman.

It is even possible for the automatic male erectile reflex to become dependent on non-sexual stimuli in adulthood if the right circumstances are devised and repeated. A French sexologist has reported the case of a man who had sex a number of times in a room lit by a green light. Eventually the man automatically had an erection whenever he saw a green light. This must have made city driving a hazardous if stimulating adventure.

More often, however, the circumstances that accompany or create an erection are complex and easily affected by other outside influences. The penis sometimes seems to have a mind of its own, becoming erect for no good reason, while at other times it will resist all the entreaties of its owner and its owner's determined companion. It used to be thought that a penis was either erect or not but research now suggests that the erectile status of a penis is constantly changing – in the same sort of way that the earth constantly has small earthquakes while big earthquakes are relatively rare – and that this status can be affected by a vast variety of influences.

What we do know is that once an erection has developed it will, on average, last two or three minutes. This is a long time compared to some animals. An elephant takes only thirty seconds to ejaculate while a chimpanzee will only manage ten seconds or so. But three minutes are as nothing compared to animals such as the ferret which have erections of up to eight hours. A dog's penis by the way, seems to stay erect for longer than it does because after penetration it swells at the base and therefore deflates very slowly after ejaculation. The swelling at the base enables the penis to stay inside the bitch for longer than would otherwise be likely.

We also know that most men have their greatest number of erections in their late teens and early twenties and that older men often stand a better chance of getting a good erection in the morning rather than at night. This is probably partly due to the fact that a night's rest helps the ageing body and that erotic dreams are more common in the early morning when sleep is light, but it may be helped by the fact that a full bladder often helps to produce a stronger erection. Unlike women, who have to learn to find sexual satisfaction (puberty for a woman merely means menstruation and other physical changes) teenage boys have sexuality thrust upon them. Erections and nocturnal emissions of semen which accompany erotic dreams (wet dreams) are an almost inevitable part of growing up for a boy.

Semen – the fluid produced when a man ejaculates – is a remarkable substance. Its primary constituent is, of course, sperm although spermatozoa don't appear in semen until a man reaches the age of about seventeen – two years after ejaculations commonly start. Men are constantly producing sperm and the storage sacs inside their testicles are kept filled with the stuff. When the sacs are full a man is probably slightly more vulnerable to stimulation than at other times. Normally, after intercourse, his storage sacs will be fully restocked in no more than two or three days. If, however, his sexual activity decreases then he will probably notice that his sexual drive will begin to fall off. The production of testosterone, the male hormone, will also fall.

But semen doesn't only contain sperm. It contains a number of other ingredients which give it its characteristic horsechestnut-pollen smell and salty taste. There are, for example, secretions from the prostate gland which stimulate the production of spermatozoa and secretions from the seminal vesicles. These various fluids contain a variety of substances including vitamin C, protein and sugar. Semen is so rich in nutrients that in some African tribes it is collected during initiation ceremonies and afterwards used as a remedy for a wide variety of ailments. Traditionally, women in apparently primitive tribes have regarded semen as a precious 'food stuff' which should be consumed at source in one way or another. Recently, scientists have backed up their claims. Today, many researchers claim that semen contains substances which will improve a woman's physical and mental health.

Semen contains two substances – serotonin and histamine – which have an effect on uterine muscles and which constrict the womb slightly. (Uterine development in women seems to be impeded when condoms are used during intercourse.) It seems that semen can also be absorbed into a woman's body through her uterus and it is possible that some of the constituents may help improve breathing and control blood pressure.

Semen is whitish, sometimes with a slightly yellow tinge and an average ejaculation contains about a teaspoonful (5mls) of fluid. The record amount measured is more than the contents of two soup spoons (31mls). Men who want to obtain a more copious ejaculate can help improve the quantity of fluid they produce by masturbating nearly but not quite to orgasm an hour or so before sex. This increases the amount of prostatic secretion. When it dries semen stiffens cloth and is difficult to wash out though it can usually be removed with a stiff brush or with a weak solution of sodium bicarbonate. Ultraviolet light makes semen stains fluorescent so beware of stains if you're planning to dance under an ultraviolet light.

When a man is young semen leaves his penis with considerable force, travelling at just under 30 m.p.h. (This means that if a 100-metre record holder got sexually aroused while running he would meet himself coming). But with age the force of ejaculation becomes less violent. The erection isn't as hard as it was and the urethra is less fully expanded. As a result the passage of sperm is impeded. The muscles which fire semen out of the penis are also weaker.

So much for the penis. Let's look at the rest of a man's equipment.

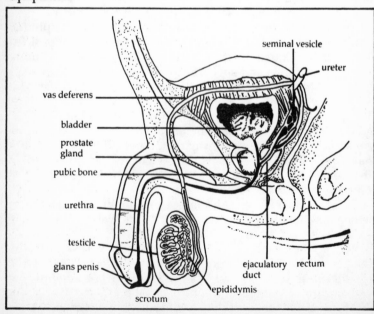

The pubic area above the base of the penis is covered with tightly curled pubic hair and straggly pubic hairs grow on the surface of the scrotum which hangs below and behind the flaccid penis and which contains the two testicles. The scrotum is a wrinkled sac of skin which is flexible and highly sensitive to touch, temperature changes and sexual stimulation. The testes hang in the scrotum because of their vulnerability to heat. When the outside temperature is cold the scrotum contracts, pulling the testes closer to the body for warmth, but when the outside temperature is hot the skin of the scrotum becomes looser, allowing the testes to move further away from the body and remain cooler.

In a male foetus the testicles develop inside the body and usually move down from near the kidneys into the scrotum before birth. Occasionally one or both testicles fail to descend properly; this problem affects approximately one in twenty boys at birth and is called cryptorchidism. Surgery or hormone treatment may be needed to bring the testicles down. If the testes stay too long inside the body the body's internal heat can kill sperm producing tissues and cause infertility. The temperature inside the scrotum is considerably cooler than the internal body temperature.

It isn't only cold weather that makes the testicles rise up: fear and sexual excitement can have the same effect. In children the testicles often go right up inside the abdomen during moments of terror. This reflex is clearly useful for adults who spend a lot of their time fighting since the testicles are exceptionally vulnerable to injury, and Japanese warriors have for centuries taken pride in being able to pull their testicles up inside their bodies when danger threatens.

Inside the scrotum the two egg-shaped testicles have two tasks: they produce male sex hormones which cause bodily changes at puberty and they also produce sperm. Each testis is attached to an epididymis where sperm are stored as they mature, and two tubes, the *vas deferens*, carry sperm from the testes to the penis. En route, attached to each side of these tubes, there are storage sacs called seminal vesicles where mature sperm are stored. These sacs are essential because the testes produce sperm all the time. On an average sort of day a healthy man will produce around 90 million sperm. That's more than enough to populate North America in three days or the whole of northern Europe in a week. Also alongside the *vas deferens* are the glands which produce the fluid which contains and nourishes the sperm during and after ejaculation.

The two testicles normally hang at different heights, with the left one usually lower than the right. This is to stop them knocking into one another.

♟♟ The Equipment in Action – Her

The first sign that a woman is responding sexually and that her body is preparing for intercourse is when her vagina becomes moist with lubricating fluid. Lubrication of the vagina can, I must quickly point out, result from many other different types of stimulus, including fear, anxiety and general excitement, but it is also the first physical sign of arousal. The lubrication starts quite quickly – usually within ten to thirty seconds of stimulation.

It used to be thought that the lubricating fluid came from the womb, but it is now known that this isn't true. After a hysterectomy – a total removal of the womb – a woman's vagina can still become moist when she is sexually aroused. The lubrication comes from several sources, most from the glands at the entrance to the vagina but some from the walls of the vagina itself in what is effectively a sort of 'sweating' reaction. When a woman is aroused blood enters the tissues around the vagina in much the same way that blood flows into the penis in a male. The fluid that seeps out into the vagina has come from congested blood vessels in the vaginal walls.

At the same time as the fluid is flowing into the vagina the clitoris begins to swell a little too; being packed with erectile tissue it swells in exactly the same way as the penis. There are changes in the breasts in this 'excitement' phase as well. Contractions of the muscle fibres around the nipples mean that the nipples become erect. Also the nipples increase in size as blood flows into them. The areolae – the areas around the nipples – become slightly swollen and in some women (particularly women who have never had children) the whole breast swells too.

When a penis enters the vagina the penis pulls on the *labia minora* and this produces some friction between the clitoral hood and the glans of the clitoris. The clitoris, as I've already explained, is packed with sensitive nerve endings and being swollen is even more responsive than usual. The outer lips – the *labia majora* – open a little wider and become swollen, moving away from the entrance to the vagina to give the penis more room. The *labia minora* also swell a little and the vaginal muscles in the first part of the vagina expand.

In addition to these specific changes in and around the vagina there are also some more general changes in the woman's body when intercourse begins. Her pulse will speed up, her blood pressure will rise and a red flush, rather like a measles rash, will often appear on her stomach and breasts. This sort of skin rash is much commoner in women than in men – three quarters of all women show some sort of flushing compared to a quarter of all men.

Sexual excitement in both men and women is said to consist of several phases. Excitement and arousal is the first. The second phase is known as the plateau and it is during this phase that a woman's body is prepared for orgasm. A number of things happen during the plateau phase. The woman's breathing rate gradually increases, her pulse and blood pressure go up even more, any flushing that has appeared on her skin will become more marked and widespread and her muscles will begin to show signs of tension. Her face, for example, will begin to show a fairly typical grimace. Her buttock muscles may tense too. Her breasts, nipples and areolae will swell even more.

Inside her vagina drops of fluid will leak from the Bartholin's glands and the tissues in and around the outer part of her vagina will swell. As the vaginal tissues swell so the vagina will grip the penis more and more tightly. The *labia minora* will darken in colour and the clitoris will steadily become more and more elevated.

The tension now builds up towards an orgasm. There are many myths and there is much confusion about how women have orgasms, how often they have them, where they come from and whose responsibility it is to see that an orgasm is obtained. The myths and the confusion have been devised and spread by countless professionals and journalists.

I think it is well worth while pointing out that whatever you may have heard or read previously an orgasm is an orgasm and it doesn't matter where it comes from. It really doesn't make any difference to the end result if an orgasm is produced by stimulation of the vagina, clitoris, breast or left big toe. In cold clinical terms an orgasm can be defined as a peak of sexual arousal which consists of uncontrollable muscle movements, a tingling, a general feeling of warmth and an indescribable sense of joy and pleasure. During an orgasm most people respond in a similar way – whatever their sex. Technically an orgasm is identical in men and women. It has been described by a physiologist as a 'mass neuronal discharge, originating in a part of the brain between the amygdala and the hypothalamus . . .' and it is accompanied by some or all of the following physical signs:

1. A progressive loss of intellectual capabilities
2. Dilatation of the pupils
3. An agonized facial expression
4. Involuntary vocalization – or shouting out loud
5. An increase in the pulse rate to somewhere between 120 and 180
6. An involuntary heavy thrusting movement of the pelvis
7. Contractions and tightening of the various muscles result- ing in gasping breathing, tightening of the fingers, spread- ing of the toes, an upward movement of the big toes, and so on.

Many people say that they have never seen their partners exhibit these signs. This may well be because one person having or approaching an orgasm will find it difficult to observe another!

During orgasm, the outer third of the vagina will usually contract rythmically too. A mild orgasm will usually be accompanied by between three and five contractions, an intense orgasm by eight to twelve contractions. The longest recorded series of contractions is twenty-five which lasted for an exhausting forty-three seconds. When these pelvic contractions take place some women say they feel as if they are ejaculating. Others say they feel that their bodies are opening up or falling from a great height. Many describe the contractions as a throbbing sensation which makes them feel warm all over. Unlike a man's, a woman's orgasm can be interrupted and continued.

Despite the theoretical stimulation of the clitoris by the movement of the penis between the *labia minora*, the majority of women do not have an orgasm directly as a result of sexual intercourse but usually need some additional manual stimulation of their clitoris. This failure to reach orgasm through straightforward intercourse produces a considerable amount of anxiety and guilt among both women and their partners.

If fully aroused and sexually excited before penetration takes place some women can reach orgasm in as little as fifteen to thirty seconds. Normally, however, a woman will take around four minutes from start to finish. This is often rather longer than a man can wait before he ejaculates and his erection starts to lose its strength, so it is hardly surprising that many women need some sort of additional stimulation of their clitoris or the area around the clitoris.

When a woman finally has an orgasm the muscle tensions that have accumulated during the last few minutes will slowly disappear. Blood will flow out of the clitoris, the *labia*, the nipples and the areolae, and all these organs and tissues will shrink back to their normal size. The sexual flush will disappear from the skin and probably be replaced by some perspiration, particularly on the hands and on the soles of the feet. The vaginal muscles will go back to normal, and the clitoris will return to its unstimulated position. At the same time the opening in the cervix will enlarge slightly to make it easier for sperm to get into the uterus.

The post-ejaculatory depression that affects women to some extent (but which seems to affect men far more dramatically) is actually a help to women who want to get pregnant because it ensures that the deposited semen won't be displaced by any more movement or by muscle contractions resulting from more sexual arousal. Gynaecologists treating women who are trying to get pregnant usually advise them to rest after sex. A man's second ejaculate will contain far fewer sperm than his first ejaculate.

Women who do not have an orgasm after being sexually aroused may, in addition to being left feeling unsatisfied and frustrated, also suffer from pain and congestion in the pelvic area. The blood vessels which have swollen and filled with blood do not empty so quickly.

👫 The Equipment in Action – Him

An erection is the first clear physical sign that a man is sexually aroused. His interest is far more difficult to disguise and far easier to interpret. But the erection of the penis (which is described in more detail on page 19) is not the only physical sign of sexual arousal. As his feeling of excitement grows other changes occur. His breathing rate will increase, his pulse and blood pressure will rise, he may acquire a sexual flush, his testes will increase in size by as much as 50 per cent and will be pulled higher into his scrotum, his nipples will become erect, the muscles of his face will show the tension he feels and his buttock muscles become tense too.

A few moments before a man ejaculates a few drops of a clear, sticky fluid will usually leak out of the end of the penis. The purpose of this liquid is to moisten the glans and to prepare the way for the flow of semen which will follow. (It is important to remember that these preliminary drops of fluid may contain sperm and may, therefore, result in pregnancy.) Immediately prior to orgasm the seminal fluid which contains the sperm will collect in the seminal vesicles. These storage organs contract rythmically, expelling their contents into the urethra at the same time as the prostate gland contracts and expels its secretions into the urethra. A bulb in the urethra near the base of the penis doubles or triples in size in order to store these fluids for a few moments.

Once a man's orgasm starts it cannot be stopped. At first, the contractions of the urethra and the prostrate gland occur at intervals of just under a second. These contractions are strong, projecting the semen outwards with considerable force, then they gradually get weaker and more and more irregular. Within a few seconds all the accumulated sperm is ejaculated, usually in five or six spurts, although the world record is believed to be twenty. Sperm leaves the end of the penis with enough force to travel several feet. The world record distance currently stands at 8 feet 8 inches (2.6 metres) and is, I suspect, likely to remain at that distance for some time to come. The ancient Hebrews used to believe that sperm that didn't come out forcefully wasn't fertile. In a way that belief is understandable – the more forcefully sperm leaves the penis the more likely it is to reach the cervix and get into the uterus where it will stand a chance of meeting an egg. In older men, the semen leaves the penis with less force and travels a considerably shorter distance.

At the moment of ejaculation a man's pulse rate, blood pressure and breathing rate all reach a peak. If he has a flush on his skin then that will deepen. His face will be contorted into a grimace; other muscles will go into spasm too. His hands will clench, his toes will spread and the muscle contractions may result in him feeling aches in his back or thighs afterwards. The outward physical signs of orgasm are the same for a man as for a woman.

As can happen with a woman, a few drops of urine may escape during orgasm – despite the existence of a valve which should, theoretically, prevent urine entering the penis. This small amount of urine will do no harm.

The erect penis will usually begin to wilt soon after the last drop of semen leaves the urethra. This shrinking process is known as detumescence. Normally the penis takes between a few seconds and three minutes to return to its fully flaccid state, and as the penis wilts so the man's sense of pleasure will mysteriously disappear. A human penis is usually withdrawn from the vagina before it subsides but in some animals this is impossible. I've already explained what happens in the dog (see page 20) but in some animals small hooks hold the penis in place and ensure that sexual intercourse ends less abruptly.

After ejaculation the blood that has filled the penis and given it strength leaves in two phases. First, the arteries which had opened up under the influence of sexual excitement become constricted again. This means that no more blood can flow into the penis. The blood that is in the penis flows out, slowly at first through the central veins which are not compressed quite so thoroughly. As soon as a little blood has flown out the tissues become decompressed and blood can flow out gradually. The first stage of detumescence is fast. The second stage tends to be much slower. This collapse of an erection normally occurs after ejaculation but it can occur if something unpleasant happens. Fear, pain, surprise or even a harsh comment from a partner can all result in an almost instantaneous disappearance of an erection

As blood flows out of the penis the testes begin to shrink and the scrotum lowers again. Blood flows out of the nipples, which get smaller, and any skin flush slowly disappears. Slowly the breathing rate returns to normal, the pulse rate drops and blood pressure falls.

For a while after an orgasm a man cannot have another erection, or even get very excited sexually, and his penis and testicles may be exceptionally sensitive and tender. This is known as the refractory period – something women don't have. The length of the refractory period varies considerably, depending on age and state of mind; anxiety, stress, disappointment or guilt can all extend it.

In addition to this physical consequence it is also common for men to feel sad or even depressed after an orgasm. The precise emotion tends to depend upon the man's relationship with his partner. If the relationship is a loving one there may be a satisfied, happy, contented, calm feeling. But if the relationship is, for example, a one-night stand then the risks, the promises and the consequences may all flood into his mind eventually producing a deep depression. Strangely, animals often respond in the same way after sex. And even artificially draining the seminal vesicles can make a man feel rather low.

Although perhaps pride, pleasure at overcoming resistance or contentment may sweeten the bitter aftertaste of sex it is common for men to feel so mentally drained and empty that they simply fall asleep. If he is with a woman he wants to impress, a man may make a determined effort to stay awake – and may find that the added stimulation makes this possible – but with a regular partner many men have great difficulty in not drifting into unconsciousness.

In those relatively rare circumstances when an erection does not lead to an orgasm a man will frequently be left not only feeling mentally unsatisfied and frustrated but also feeling some pain from prostatic engorgement.

Chapter 2

 # What Other People Do

Scores of major surveys about sex have been commissioned in the last decade or two, and statistics about the number of times men and women have sex get the most publicity despite being the least interesting. Quantity is not all that important to most couples and comparing how many times you do it is both pretty boring and likely to add to the feelings of inadequacy that affects just about all of us. (Statistics showing how often people 'do it' are notoriously inaccurate anyway; the one thing people lie about consistently is how often they make love!)

So, ignoring statistics of quantity, I've studied twenty-five of the biggest surveys pub'ished in the last two decades, fed the results into my computer and discovered some astonishing things about men and women. There are two advantages to using information from so many surveys. First, I have a much wider range of questions than the ordinary survey (how many surveys include 150 questions?). And, second, my results are more accurate than individual surveys since my figures relate to thousands of men and women, not just a few hundred. However, when I say '81 per cent of women', I do of course mean 81 per cent of the women questioned.

So, here it is – the survey of surveys. I think you'll find the information comforting and reassuring as well as fascinating!

1. 81 per cent of women say that wearing sexy clothes helps them to get into the mood for sex
2. 20 per cent of women like making love naked but another 20 per cent make love naked to please their partners
3. Half of all the women whose partners like them to wear sexy nighties oblige by wearing sexy nighties in bed
4. 70 per cent of the women whose partners like them to wear stockings and suspenders in bed do wear stockings and suspenders in bed
5. 70 per cent of the women whose partners like them to dress up in special clothes (eg nurse's or waitress's uniforms) do so
6. 75 per cent of women say that sexual fantasies are an enjoyable, important and satisfying part of their sex lives
7. Of the women who have fantasies, 60 per cent have romantic fantasies and 40 per cent have fantasies in which they are seduced (large numbers progress to more erotic, overtly physical fantasies as they approach orgasm)
8. 43 per cent of married women have affairs
9. Less than half of the women who have affairs enjoy them
10. 40 per cent of women say that having children at home inhibits their sexual desire
11. 70 per cent of women say that having children at home reduces their sexual activity
12. 70 per cent of women enjoy flirting with men other than their regular partners
13. 63 per cent of women enjoy erotic films and magazines
14. 75 per cent of women admit that they would use sex in order to 'buy' affection from their partner
15. 20 per cent of women have posed for nude photographs
16. 20 per cent of women have made love at work
17. 70 per cent of women have made love out of doors
18. 67 per cent of women with their own homes still enjoy

making love in a car
19. 10 per cent of women have made love on a train
20. 80 per cent of women say that they would definitely use a condom if having sex with a new partner
21. 40 per cent of women say that they wouldn't *not* have sex if they didn't have a condom available
22. 25 per cent of women still feel too embarrassed to buy condoms in a shop
23. 3 per cent of women have never had sex
24. Only 26 per cent of women regularly have orgasms during intercourse
25. 24 per cent of women never have orgasms during intercourse
26. 16 per cent of women only have orgasms during intercourse when they are also stimulated by hand
27. 12 per cent of women never have orgasms
28. 82 per cent of women masturbate regularly
29. 96 per cent of women who masturbate orgasm regularly during masturbation
30. 73 per cent of women masturbate by lying on their backs and stimulating their clitoral and vulval areas with their hands or with a vibrator
31. 5.5 per cent of women who masturbate do so while lying on their stomachs
32. 2 per cent of women masturbate with the aid of a shower attachment
33. 3 per cent of women masturbate by pressing their thighs together rhythmically
34. 4 per cent of women masturbate by pressing their clitoral and vulval areas against a soft object such as a pillow, cushion or item of clothing
35. Only 3 per cent of women complain that their partner's penis is too small
36. Most of the married women who have affairs are unfaithful because they feel deprived emotionally rather than sexually
37. 17 per cent of women prefer to have sex with the light on
38. 54 per cent of women prefer to have sex in the dark
39. 29 per cent don't mind whether the light is on or off
40. 60 per cent of women are turned on by a muscular male body but most women think that a firm bottom is a man's most important feature

41. The majority of women think that a flat stomach is a man's second most important feature
42. 90 per cent of women like being undressed by their lovers
43. 50 per cent of men have bought sexy clothes (most commonly stockings and suspenders) for their partners
44. 50 per cent of men have had sex in a public place
45. 65 per cent of men with their own homes still like making love in a car
46. 80 per cent of men say that they would definitely use a condom if they had sex with a new partner
47. 40 per cent of men say they wouldn't stop or *not* have sex just because they didn't have a condom available
48. 25 per cent of men feel too embarrassed to buy condoms in a shop
49. 69 per cent of men find sexy nighties alluring
50. 50 per cent of men like their partners to be naked when they actually make love
51. 40 per cent of men like their partners to wear stockings and suspenders while making love
52. 7 per cent of men like their partners to dress up in 'special' clothes (eg nurse's or waitress's uniform) to make love
53. 55 per cent of men complain that their partners are usually too tired to make love
54. 30 per cent of women lose their virginity before the age of 16 and 50 per cent by 17
55. 64 per cent of women have had six or more lovers
56. 17 per cent of women have had twenty-five or more lovers
57. 62 per cent of women are willing to have sex on the first date
58. 17 per cent of women have had group sex
59. 16 per cent of women have had at least one lesbian experience
60. 43 per cent of women use vibrators
61. Only 61 per cent of men say that they never have problems getting an erection
62. 16 per cent of married men have extra-marital sex at least once in their first year of marriage
63. 72 per cent of men who have been married two years or more have been unfaithful
64. 84 per cent of women perform fellatio on their partners and 65 per cent of those women enjoy it
65. 81 per cent of men perform cunnilingus on their partners

and 70 per cent of the women enjoy it

66. 10 per cent of men sleep in the nude
67. 45 per cent of men prefer sex with the lights on
68. 29 per cent of men prefer sex in the dark
69. 26 per cent of men don't mind whether the lights are on or not
70. 2 per cent of women sleep in the nude
71. 50 per cent of men think that women should be allowed the same sexual freedom as men; 50 per cent do not
72. 50 per cent of women think that women should be allowed the same sexual freedom as men; 50 per cent do not
73. 82 per cent of women say that their first sexual experience was confined to mild petting
74. 6 per cent of women say that their first sexual experience was full intercourse
75. 12 per cent of women say that their first sexual experience was confined to heavy petting which led to an orgasm for one or both partners
76. 75 per cent of women who are divorced or widowed have sex outside of marriage before they get married again
77. 18 per cent of women found their first sexual experience thrilling
78. 18 per cent of women found their first sexual experience painful and upsetting
79. The majority of women do not reach orgasm during their first sexual experience but most say that the experience made them feel grown up and wanted
80. 75 per cent of seventy-year-old men still have sex regularly and 92 per cent still think about sex regularly
81. 36 per cent of eighty-year-old men still have sex regularly and 61 per cent still think about it
82. 70 per cent of women say that they make the first move in bed at least some of the time
83. 90 per cent of men and women with sexual experience have tried more than one sexual position
84. Women with jobs outside the home make love more often than housewives
85. 47 per cent of women have unsatisfactory sex lives
86. 68 per cent of men and women regard the bedroom as the most suitable place for sex
87. 33 per cent of men and women would rather watch TV in bed than have sex

88. 69 per cent of women wear perfume every day
89. 18 per cent of single women in their thirties haven't had sex for more than three years
90. 50 per cent of single women have had affairs with married men
91. 48 per cent of women admit to wearing sexy clothes deliberately to attract men
92. 40 per cent of women regularly fake an orgasm
93. 33 per cent of men would like the partners to be more experimental
94. 60 per cent of men never refuse sex when approached by a woman
95. 25 per cent of women never refuse sex when approached by a man
96. 30 per cent of men say that they have at some time worried about the size of their penis
97. 35 per cent of women complain that men fall asleep immediately after sex
98. 26 per cent of men complain that women want to talk after sex
99. 44 per cent of women complain that men spend too little time on foreplay
100. 18 per cent of men say that women spend too little time on foreplay
101. 23 per cent of men complain that women take too long to reach orgasm
102. 80 per cent of men are turned off when a woman wears too much make-up
103. 60 per cent of men like women to shave their legs, 30 per cent like women to leave their legs hairy and 10 per cent don't give a damn
104. 50 per cent of men find pregnant women exceptionally sexy
105. 25 per cent of men dislike going out with beautiful women – they find them too frightening
106. 20 per cent of men find intelligent women scary
107. 10 per cent of men feel uncomfortable when meeting women who have well-paid jobs
108. 40 per cent of men like being bitten during sex
109. Most men look at a woman's legs before they look at her breasts
110. 40 per cent of men who go to church regularly like sex but

80 per cent of non-churchgoers enjoy it

111. Only 20 per cent of men think that sex is the most important pleasure in their lives. For the rest sport, television and drinking with their mates are more popular activities

112. 17 per cent of men are turned on by ankle chains

113. Only 6 per cent of women feel that sex is the most important part of a relationship

114. 26 per cent of men and 5 per cent of women have watched a strip show or live sex show

115. 26 per cent of women say that they have sex so that they will not be alone

116. 3 per cent of men say that they have sex so that they will not be alone

117. 34 per cent of women enjoy talking dirty during sex

118. 42 per cent of men enjoy talking dirty during sex

119. 37 per cent of women scream and shout during sex

120. 12 per cent of men scream and shout during sex

121. 76 per cent of men tell their partner what they like during sex

122. 68 per cent of women tell their partner what they like during sex

123. 34 per cent of women like to wait for at least a month after the first date before having sex

124. 21 per cent of men like to wait a month after the first date before having sex

125. 31 per cent of men lose their virginity before the age of sixteen

126. 85 per cent of men have lost their virginity by the time they reach the age of nineteen

127. 34 per cent of men who are married or involved in a steady relationship tell their partners that they love them at least once a day

128. 25 per cent of men who are married or in a steady relationship rarely or never say 'I love you'

129. 60 per cent of men wish that their partner would make the first move more often

130. Only 3 per cent of men have ever turned down a sexual suggestion made by a partner

131. The average man and woman make love once and possibly twice a week (at most). Most experts believe that this figure is probably too high since people are reluctant to admit to

less when being questioned

132. Only one in twenty steady couples have sex every day
133. 26 per cent of women say that power and money are a sexual turn-on for them
134. 15 per cent of men have posed for nude photographs
135. 90 per cent of men like giving and receiving oral sex
136. 63 per cent of single girls say that they have one-night stands not expecting them to lead to a long-term romance
137. 14 per cent of men have visited a prostitute at least once
138. 66 per cent of men sometimes have difficulties in getting an erection or having an orgasm
139. 93 per cent of men have made love in the living room
140. 92 per cent of women have made love in the living room
141. 6 per cent of women have made love on a water bed
142. 5 per cent of men have made love on a water bed
143. 1 per cent of women have made love in an aeroplane
144. 2 per cent of men have made love in an aeroplane
145. 66 per cent of women say that they would marry their husbands again
146. 50 per cent of single women aged between eighteen and thirty-five have seduced at least one man
147. 55 per cent of single women have had sex during a lunch break
148. 35 per cent of men have fantasies while making love
149. 75 per cent of men are turned on sexually if they think a woman is wearing stockings and suspenders
150. More than 50 per cent of men and women say that friendship is the most important part of a relationship

Chapter 3

Turning Your Partner On

How To Be Irresistible

If you've ever wished that you could be sexier, or you've ever envied friends who are always surrounded by admiring members of the opposite sex, then this chapter could change your life.

Whether you are struggling to find a new partner or to revive an established relationship that now has all the zip and excitement of a well-worn pair of old slippers, there are many things that you can do to make yourself more sexually attractive. It's not something you either are or are not; looking sexy (which doesn't mean being garish, obvious or 'cheap') is something you can learn. It is often just as important to make an effort to look good in a long-term relationship as when 'courting'. Many marriages begin to fail after a year or two because the partners no longer see each other as sexy. It's difficult for her to see him as a sex object when he's spent the day clearing out the guttering or crawling around in the loft and he's too tired to bother. It's equally difficult for him to get sexually aroused when he sees her hunched over a sink full of dirty pots and pans every day. So here are some ground rules.

Pick the right clothes . . .

For him: Only flashy, young, inexperienced men wear tight trousers; something slightly baggy and comfortable is better. Choose clothes that make you look relaxed. Wear a sports jacket and trousers rather than a suit. If you wear jeans then choose jeans that are faded and well-worn but not ripped or dirty. Light, pastel colours are good. Clothes that contrast are a good start; for example, a light jacket and a darker shirt. Ties should be fairly plain but brightly coloured. Hats are good but gloves are not. Don't look as if you've spent hours preparing.

For her: Either wear clothes that are loose and billowy and very feminine or clothes that are tight and figure-hugging. Have a wide variety of different clothes rather than variations on the same theme. Try a smart suit worn with a white blouse or a fitted jumper and a skirt so tight that you have difficulty walking. Try flowery, summer dresses, sleeveless and low cut. Avoid anything ankle length and stick to skirts and dresses which are cut above the knee. If you wear trousers wear them tight. Red and black are the most sexually provocative colours. Fabrics such as silk and satin and leather are sexier than cotton or wool. To look sexy you need to emphasize the things that make women different to men so don't be shy about emphasizing your curves.

🏃🏃 . . . and the right accessories

For him: A signet ring is OK but not a wedding ring. If you wear a belt choose something slim in leather, fastened with a small neat buckle; don't go for anything broad with an ornate fastener. Don't wear an ear-ring. Your watch should have a traditional face; digital is not good. Don't, whatever you do, have pens or a handkerchief in your top pocket. Never wear braces (whatever the fashion writers may say). Don't select button-down shirt collars and don't use a tie pin. Prefer buttons to ostentatious cuff-links.

For her: Carry a small handbag and never wear a headscarf. Wear several rings on your fingers and always wear ear-rings, large dangly ones are best. Usually try to show some cleavage. If you want to look very special draw attention to the cleavage by wearing something bright and dangly round your neck, a chunky necklace for example. If you wear a brooch it should be a bright one designed to draw attention to the breast upon which it is pinned.

🏃🏃 Hair is important

For him: Whether you wear it long or short wear it neat; even if tousled it should be controlled tousle. One of the first things a woman looks at (after a man's bottom) is his hair so take great care with it. Always carry a comb (but don't use it obviously). Avoid a beard, moustache and sideburns; cleanshaven is best. Designer stubble is out. If you must wear a moustache grow something huge and shaggy rather than neat and trimmed. Sideburns suggest a man trying to recapture his youth. A beard suggests a man who is more interested in men than women. Hair oil is out – it will make you look too manicured.

For her: Sexy hair is either very long or very short. Spend hours trying to make your hair look as though you've just got out of bed. Blonde, or blonde highlights, really is sexy. Wax your legs regularly. Trim away excess pubic hair. If you shave underarm hair do it regularly, otherwise let it grow.

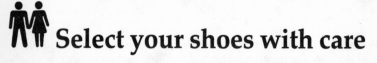 Select your shoes with care

For him: Wear something with lots of polish. Pumps and trainers are definitely out for the man trying to look sexy. Maybe choose something a little unusual – shoes with pointed toes, unusual patterns or bright colours. The smaller man will wear a shoe with a heel (but nothing obvious or excessive) to make him look taller.

For her: Definitely wear high heels; the thinner and higher the heel the sexier the effect. Even if you are with a smaller man don't leave the high heels behind. Choose red if you want to offer maximum impact. The woman who is full of mystery and promise will choose black.

Think about your underwear

For him: No vest, definitely no vest. Below the belt you should wear either skimpy briefs or boxer shorts. And they should be brightly coloured or patterned. Muddy-coloured Y-fronts are definitely out. The sexy man's socks will be short and brightly coloured.

For her: Choose your underwear with him in mind. Lacy half-cup bra, skimpy lacy knickers and stockings and suspenders for a special evening. If you're feeling really racy the stockings should be seamed. If you must wear tights (a turn-off) make sure they are seamed or patterned but not coloured. Black or white underwear is sensual; red is raunchy and unashamedly physical. The ultimate female sex bomb wears absolutely no underwear at all – nothing but three dabs of perfume in strategic spots. If you want to drive him wild tell him what you're wearing (make him guess) or not wearing beforehand, when there's nothing he can do about it.

Use perfume sparingly

Many women, and men, use far too much perfume. A little perfume can be a real turn-on. Too much can be a massive turn-off. Don't drown yourself in eau de cologne or aftershave. Remember we all produce our own special, sexually attractive smells when we are aroused. Those smells are *really* irresistible. Use too much artificial perfume and you'll drown them.

Watch how you walk

For him: Pull in your stomach, stick out your chest and stand as upright as you can. Don't slouch; it's important to 'walk tall' and make the most of your height. Walk with a bit of a swagger if you can master it without looking silly, or drunk.

For her: Women have a natural wiggle due to the shape of their pelvis and balance of their hips; accentuate the wiggle by rolling your hips, deliberately and provocatively pushing your bottom from side to side as you walk. This type of walk works equally well with a tight pair of trousers, a tight short skirt or a loose, billowy, flouncy dress. Unless you are very tall try to make the most of your height. Pull in your stomach and pull back your shoulders in order to push out your chest.

The way you stand and sit is important

For him: Stand with your thumbs in your belt or with your hands on your hips. Stand with your body facing the woman you're trying to impress, and with at least one foot pointing directly at her. Lean forwards slightly towards the woman you fancy. When you sit keep your legs wide apart or your knees pointing directly at the woman you're interested in.

For her: Stand with your body facing the man you fancy. You should stand with one foot pointing directly at him. If you want to accentuate the size and shape of your bosom push your shoulders back, otherwise lean forwards slightly. Stand with one hand on your hip or, if you have a belt, with a thumb tucked into it. When you sit, either have your knees pointing at the man you're interested in or sit with your legs slightly apart. Stroke your own thigh occasionally and apparently carelessly. Hitching up your skirt or dress an inch as you sit down may sound corny but it works (even younger members of the British Royal Family have been known to resort to this old trick when struggling a little for attention).

👫 Use your eyes

For him: Try to catch her eye and then hold her gaze for as long as you can. Look straight at her. Don't forget to smile, but not grin or grimace.

For her: Use make-up to attract attention to your eyes. Mascara and eyeliner make eyes look bigger and more irresistible. When you know you've got him hooked and he's looking at you, look down and then glance shyly upwards or sideways. The Princess of Wales uses this trick for flirting with everyone from pop stars to photographers.

For both of you: Given a choice of two identical partners most of us will choose the individual whose eyes have the biggest pupils. Your eyes really can make all the difference. How can you acquire bigger pupils? Easy. First, take a real interest in the people you meet. Listen to what they say. Stay alert and awake. Second, avoid bright lights. Your pupils shrink when the lights are bright. Keep your back to any lamps. Turn down lighting. Next, if you wear spectacles, take them off when you meet. Spectacles seal off your eyes and make eye to eye contact difficult. But the very act of taking them off attracts attention to your eyes and can, therefore, work in your favour. Finally, just before you meet fantasize about him or her. Try to build up an exciting image. Your heart will beat faster, your face will flush slightly and your pupils will dilate. All these subtle physical signs will help to turn him or her on. Your fantasy dream play will turn you into a real sex bomb.

Use movement and touch

For him: Adjust and straighten your tie from time to time. Run your fingers through your hair.

For her: Touch yourself constantly. Check your make-up, refresh your lipstick and tidy your hair every few minutes. Try a casual toss of your head to flick your hair back. Lick your lips and keep your mouth slightly open. The really sexy woman will give her intentions away by fondling anything phallic that she can lay her hands on – running her fingers up and down a pen or wine glass stem for example. Cross and uncross your legs repeatedly, showing plenty of knee and try slipping one foot in and out of your shoe. If you're holding something try to hold it in such a way that you expose the inside of your wrist.

For both of you: Remember that touch can be a tremendous turn-on. It need only be the lightest touch for the briefest of moments. Let your fingers touch when you hand over a glass. Hold him (or her) lightly on the arm as you move through a crowd. Put your hand in hers (his) as you cross the road. If he (she) has a headache offer to help with a massage.

Turn your partner on with your voice – and what you say

For him: Lower your voice slightly, speak quietly and confidently.

For her: Speak in a slightly different voice when you want to project a sexy image. Lower your voice and adopt a rather husky tone. Try to resist the temptation to raise your voice and speak in a 'little girl lost' tone. It probably won't work and there's a real danger that you end up sounding very silly.

For both of you: Share your secrets and encourage your partner to confide in you. Let your emotions show a little. Don't be afraid to show that you are sad, happy or angry. If you cover up your emotions completely then you'll appear placid, flat and boring. You certainly won't be an irresistible lover. But be warned! Don't *overdo* it. To be irresistible you must get the balance right. And the emotions you show must always be honest. Don't be afraid to speak out or stand up for things you believe in – but don't be unnecessarily argumentative, forceful or controversial for the sake of it. Try to avoid issues like politics or religion where it is too easy to offend rather than stimulate. Genuine passion for a cause you believe in can make you charismatic instead of merely charming.

One final thought: don't talk about sex, and especially not about your sexual conquests or experiences, unless you are with someone you know *very* well.

Courtship and Foreplay

Do you remember that awful joke about the Australian woman who moaned about her husband's sexual technique, or lack of it. She complained, that his idea of foreplay was to yell, 'Brace yourself!'

Most men probably aren't quite that bad but there is no doubt that one of the things women most commonly complain about is that their partners just don't spend enough time on foreplay.

'I'm lying in bed or sitting on the sofa and suddenly this hand starts squeezing my breast,' one patient of mine explained. 'There's no warning and no attempt to get me into the mood.'

It's usually men who are guilty of over-eagerness and of a lack of understanding, but it isn't *only* men. Some women are as guilty as men and, wrongly assuming that men are always ready for action, will reach for a man's trouser fly with no warning and then express profound disappointment when there is no appropriate response.

The truth is that for many people of both sexes foreplay is as important as, sometimes even more important than, actual intercourse.

There are exceptions, of course. Occasionally, a couple will want to plunge straight into steamy sex without any preliminaries at all. If they have been parted for some time anticipation will perhaps have raised expectations. Buttons will fly and material will rip as they seek out one another's bodies. Just as there are some people who will always want to run straight into the sea without pausing to dip a toe in the water first, so there will be some lovers who will find foreplay frustrating and unnecessary. But they are the exceptions.

Most people need to get into the mood to enjoy sex. And that means more than just a few moments of rough fondling. It means thought, care and tenderness. It means spending a little time on preparation.

Think back to your very first date. You were probably nervous. You were almost certainly excited too. You made sure that you looked your best. You thought carefully about what to wear and what to say. You held hands, had a glass of something, talked, put your arms around one another, ate a meal, relaxed, admired one another, murmured sweet nothings into one another's ears and only then did you kiss.

How Not To Turn Your Partner Off

When I worked as a general practitioner I listened to a steady stream of women telling me that they wanted to have their breasts improved with plastic surgery. After a while I became convinced that there probably isn't a woman in the entire world who is completely satisfied with the size and shape of her bosom. If the supply of plastic surgeons rose to meet the demand for surgery there wouldn't be a doctor anywhere in the world doing anything except make big boobs smaller and small boobs bigger.

Each one of those women was convinced that the first and only thing men look at when they meet a woman is her chest. They were nearly all wrong. Although men like talking about breasts (and looking at photographs of them in newspapers and magazines) when they come face to face with a real-life woman the size of her breasts is about as vital to the impending relationship as the size of her feet.

Not that it's only women who worry about the wrong things. Men do too.

I'd been qualified as a doctor no more than forty-five minutes when I first met a man who was worried about the size of his penis. He wanted to know what he could do to make it larger. He, like thousands of other men, was worried that no woman would want him unless he could offer her an organ as big as a baseball bat.

All this anxiety is, perhaps, not all that surprising. There is a huge industry out there busily involved in telling women and men what to worry about. Read the advertisements carefully and you'll be convinced the things men look for when they meet a woman are split ends and cracked nail polish. Men, on the other hand, are encouraged to worry about the way they smell and the quantity of hair on their heads.

The truth is, however, that just about every survey ever published shows that men really don't care much about what a woman's hair looks like. There are some hair styles and colours that are slightly more attractive than others, and that may add to an overall picture, but I rather doubt if any relationship has ever been severed or has ever failed to get going because he didn't like the fact that she wasn't wearing hairspray.

I once knew a girl who worried incessantly about making sure that she satisfied her boyfriend's every whim and wish. Or at least all the whims and hopes she thought he might have. Before each date she would spend hours in the bathroom scrubbing herself clean. When she'd finally made sure that every square inch, and every nook and cranny, was sanitized, sterilized and deodorized she carefully squirted perfume onto her body. She would spend ten minutes scrubbing her teeth with her powerful peppermint toothpaste and then she'd gargle with an antiseptic mouthwash. That done she'd spend an hour on her hair and another thirty minutes with the eyebrow tweezers.

It took her half a day to get ready for each date and when the romance ended she was heartbroken. She couldn't understand what had gone wrong. As he broke the sad news to her she tearfully begged him to explain why it was ending. He told her that he couldn't stand women who were always late. For him hanging around for an hour outside a cinema was a far bigger turn-off than less than perfect eyebrows.

Another girl I knew had a magnificent body, a beautiful face and a wonderful personality. She didn't have an ounce of unwanted fat anywhere. Her skin was soft and blemish free. Her hair was blonde, silky and shoulder length. Her breasts looked as if they'd been sculpted by da Vinci or Michelangelo. Her legs drew gasps of admiration from everyone who saw them. She had the figure of a screen siren, the face of an angel and the personality of a saint. But every date she ever had was a one-night stand. No one ever wanted to take her out again. She had gum disease and when she opened her mouth the stench was appalling. Her breath smelt so bad that even men who were hypnotized by her looks couldn't face the thought of another evening within ten miles of her.

When it comes down to it the things that turn members of the opposite sex off or on are very simple to understand. It's not the surface detail, the determination to look perfect, that matters. It's the whole package – character, aspirations, achievements – combined with a balanced attempt to smell and look clean and presentable in whatever way suits you best.

Before I started to write this chapter I conducted a straightforward survey of my own to try and find out exactly what turned men off women and precisely what made women go 'ugh'. I found that the things that act as the biggest sexual turn-offs are the same things that are offensive in every other area of life. Dirty fingernails, breath that stinks of alcohol, cigarettes, garlic or rotting teeth, and the stench of old decomposing sweat are the real turn-offs. So, generally are arrogance, an overbearing manner and no sense of humour. When they're looking for an intimate relationship (or an evening of sex with a long-term partner) both men and women are more likely to be turned off by poor hygiene, which you can help, than by dry hair or an unfashionable figure, which you can't. And, inevitably, the real turn-on is someone who is a good listener, who is interesting, witty and charming.

The things about men that turn women off

1. Having bad breath
2. Having a smelly, unwashed body
3. Pretending to be in love on a first date, or pretending to be in love when they can't possibly be
4. Being fat, with an overhanging belly
5. Wanting to make love while drunk
6. Wearing socks in bed
7. Wearing underclothes in bed
8. Slumping in front of the television all evening, saying nothing at all, then suddenly becoming randy as soon as they get into bed
9. Wearing vast quantities of foul smelling aftershave
10. Always rolling over and falling asleep the minute he's come
11. Not cutting his finger nails, and then lacerating her sensitive bits
12. Not shaving, and having painful stubble
13. Being unable to have a cuddle or a kiss without wanting to have sex
14. Never saying 'I love you'
15. Smelling of beer. And drinking too much
16. Spending no time at all on foreplay and then being too violent too quickly. Stampeding the clitoris
17. Never telling her how wonderful she looks, never fondling

her, kissing her or caressing her
18. Having a dirty, smelly penis and expecting oral sex
19. Telling smutty jokes, especially when they aren't even funny
20. Being boring and having no sense of humour

The things about women that turn men off

1. Endlessly preening themselves and then complaining if their make-up gets smudged
2. Never making a move; always leaving it to him to make the first move
3. Showing no enthusiasm when he gets excited about something
4. Just lying there while he does all the work in bed
5. Never wearing the sexy clothes he bought for her
6. Always making excuses for not having sex
7. Refusing to make love anywhere new
8. Refusing to make love with the lights on
9. Refusing to try anything exciting
10. Never telling him what a wonderful lover he is
11. Wearing rollers and a hairnet in bed or around the house
12. Wearing thermal underwear
13. Getting into bed with face cream on
14. Only ever wearing make-up when visitors are expected
15. Having no sense of humour
16. Moaning about the leaky guttering, the neighbours or the shelf in the bathroom just when he starts to get affectionate
17. Pushing him away when he tries something – without telling him what she would really like
18. Smelling of garlic or onions
19. Having bad breath
20. Smelling as though she needs a bath

Sexual Etiquette
Choosing the right place

Most of the time most people make love in the bedroom. But the bedroom isn't always the best place. Sometimes the walls are too thin and you may be inhibited by the thought that neighbours, in-laws or children can hear every twang of the mattress springs, every gasp of delight and every groan of pleasure. And if the door doesn't lock there is always the risk that someone may come in at a crucial moment.

If you have no children and you do not share your home with anyone else then just about anywhere can be the 'right place': living room, kitchen, bathroom, guest bedroom or even the hallway. But if you're unmarried and your evenings of passion are confined to the sofa in someone else's front room then you're unlikely to feel as uninhibited as you'd like to feel.

If you're young and or adventurous and agile then a motor car can be as exciting and stimulating a place as anywhere, as well as being cosy and private. But gear levers and hand brakes are often positioned effectively enough to be classified as contraceptives.

In films, love-making often looks wonderful on a beach with the tide coming in and the surf splashing on the sand. But in real life beaches are hardly ever deserted and your romantic feeling is unlikely to be enhanced when a small boy asks if you've seen his beach ball. Besides sand gets into every crevice imaginable and can be an irritant for days afterwards.

If your sex life is troubled, unsatisfactory or unsuccessful the right place will be somewhere warm and private and comfortable where you are unlikely to be interrupted. It may be a hotel room where you can recapture past memories and escape from the reality of blocked drains, electricity bills and demanding children.

If your relationship has hit a bad patch then you may want to recapture the magic of your courtship by spending an evening out, starting with a meal in a restaurant, going on to cuddle in the back row of the local cinema and ending up in a shop doorway.

If you've both become bored with your sex life, if it is too predictable and too ordinary, then the right place might be the kitchen table, the workbench in the garage, the back lawn at midnight or a local beauty spot at dawn.

Choosing the right time

Electricity in general and television in particular have ruined sex for most people. Electric lights and non-stop television encourage us to stay up late at night reading, working or watching whatever happens to be on. It's hardly surprising that the biggest jumps in the birthrate occur nine months after every major power cut. And even when they are in bed, electric blankets mean that people don't need to snuggle together to keep warm on long, dark, cold winter nights.

Some people make love late at night when they're finally bored with the television. They're tired, and it's hardly surprising that things don't exactly 'go with a bang'. He'll probably have difficulty in getting a good erection. When he finally does manage it he'll probably ejaculate very quickly. Then he'll fall asleep, whether she's satisfied or not. When she gets into bed exhausted after a busy day she'll probably find it difficult to get aroused. By the time she's ready he'll be finished and snoring.

There is a real risk that when a couple make love last thing at night they'll both end up disappointed and frustrated.

If you really want to make love properly it's important to choose the time carefully. Life isn't like the movies when any time is the right time!

Why not try the early morning? Sexual desire is often high then and both partners will probably find it relatively easy to get aroused. Best of all try a morning at the weekend when you don't have to worry about rushing out to work.

Many couples with children worry about the kids wandering in. That problem is easily solved by putting a lock on the bedroom door and perhaps hanging a 'Do Not Disturb' notice on the outside doorknob. Incidentally a small bolt – that anyone can fit – is just as useful as a complicated and expensive lock.

If early morning doesn't seem right try going to bed earlier in the evening. If there's something on TV that you really don't want to miss – and you haven't got a video – then go up very early so that you can come down later to watch your programme. If you have young children and they won't go to sleep early then get a friend to look after them for the evening, or the night. You can return the favour another night. If your children are older they'll probably need no encouragement to go round to see their friends for a few hours. Even if they don't, you will do them no harm by insisting that you want to spend some time alone together.

Should all these possibilities be impractical then maybe you need to plan ahead a little. Arrange for the children to stay with friends or relatives and book a room at a favourite hotel for a night or two. Rested and relaxed you may well find that your sex life is revived.

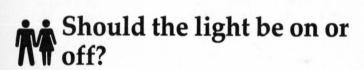 Should the light be on or off?

Some people like doing it with the light on. Others hate being seen, or hate seeing anyone else naked and insist on making love in the dark. If the two of you have opposing fancies then try a compromise: put a low-intensity bulb into a bedside-table light and fit it with a heavy shade.

It is normally women rather than men who worry about making love with the lights on. Often it is not because they are embarrassed about their own bodies but because they are worried about how they will respond when they see their male partner naked. There are naked women everywhere these days – on television, in films and in magazines and newspapers. We all get used to seeing naked female bodies. But there are relatively few opportunities for a woman to get to know what to expect when a man is naked. Some have never seen a limp penis at all. Others are startled, even frightened, when they see an erect penis or when they see a penis grow before their eyes.

The answer is to find a suitable compromise. Keep the lights on, if suitably subdued, but make love under the duvet. Encourage her, or him, to take a peek with the lights out completely. Let her, or him, get accustomed to nudity gradually and all those fears will gently disappear.

👫 Don't Be Shy About Touching

Most of us touch each other far too little. We cuddle too little. We kiss too little. We don't hold each other enough.

And yet touching is very therapeutic, even necessary. When small children aren't touched and held they quickly become depressed and stop eating. The child who is untouched and unloved may die through love starvation. When we are held and touched we know that we are loved and wanted. Children who are deprived of love when they are small often grow up with deep-rooted psychological or emotional problems. They may become promiscuous in their constant, ever-lasting, never-satisfied search for love.

But it isn't only babies and children who benefit from lots of touching and cuddling. Researchers all around the world have shown that people of all ages can benefit from sharing a warm, caring relationship. Insurance companies in America have found that if a wife kisses her husband goodbye when he goes off to work every morning he will be less likely to have a car accident on the way to the office or the factory. He will, on average, live five years longer than if she doesn't give him a morning kiss. Without physical signs of affection we become more brittle, less emotionally stable and more susceptible to fear, pressure and distress.

And, of course, the right sort of touch, in the right place, at the right time, can be extremely arousing.

Some people erroneously imagine that the only place to touch one another during foreplay is immediately below the belt. Wrong. The average human body is covered with approximately two square metres of skin. Some of that skin contains areas of special sexual sensitivity – the genital areas and lips, for example, the so-called erogenous zones – but any piece of skin on your body can become an erogenous zone if it is stimulated in the right way or if the right messages have passed that way before. Erogenous zones vary enormously from one individual to another and this variety is largely due to the fact that we all do different things to one another and we all respond in different ways. One man may love having his back stroked. Another may go wild with delight if you stroke his chest. One woman can have six different erogenous areas with six different lovers. It's no exaggeration to say that you can regard the skin as a complex and massive organ of sexual response; it is certainly an organ of sexual communication. Some woman can have an orgasm if they have their eyebrows stroked or if a lover blows onto their pubic hair. Both sexes appreciate being touched, held, licked, nibbled, pinched (gently), slapped (gently), played with and stroked.

Where do you start?

It really doesn't matter. Experiment a little.

Both men and women tend to be wonderfully sensitive on their nipples, in and around their navels, in their armpits, inside their upper thighs, at the nape of their necks, along the length of their spines and on their buttocks.

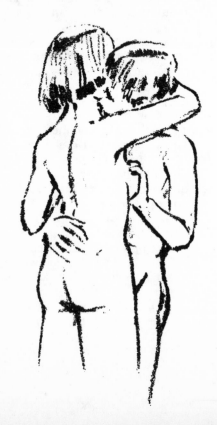

Men are often especially sensitive around their ears. Women often have erogenous zones on their throats and at the back of their knees.

Begin by just dragging your fingernails gently across the skin. Move your fingers alternately slowly and then quickly, in circles and in spirals, first this way and then that way. Stroke and massage along each different possible erogenous zone. Touch the stomach, the thighs, the backs of the knees and around the navel. Scratch the palms of both hands lightly with your nails. Blow in his, or her, ear and on her, or his, spine. Lick the most responsive spots and then blow on them. Penetrate his, or her, body symbolically be moving your finger rythmically into and out of his, or her, navel, ear or mouth.

Learn to kiss properly. Relax your mouth, let your lips go limp. Then kiss everywhere that you've touched. Practise on the palm of your hand to see the difference between a hard, clenched kiss and a soft, limp, thoroughly relaxed kiss. Brush her, or his, skin with your lips. Drag your lips along his, or her, most erogenous zones.

Some areas may be too sensitive for you to touch for long. A few women find it annoying or painful to have their nipples sucked or fondled (although the sensitivity of the nipples may vary enormously with the time of the month).

Once you've worked your way around his, or her, body, move in on the most erogenous bits. For women the clitoris is often the most sensitive part, followed by the inner lips of the vagina (the *labia minora)* and the outer lips (the *labia majora).* Some women may find one side of their vagina more sensitive than the other.

For men the most sensitive spot is usually the *frenulum,* the small piece of skin on the underside of the penis where the glans meets the shaft. Next comes the tip of the penis, the edge of the glans, the shaft and the testicles.

Both men and women are usually very sensitive in the area between the genitalia and the anus and both are also very sensitive to touch in and around the anus.

If you are shy about touching his or her sexual organs, say so. Try touching gently for a second or so at a time. Be as cautious as you like. You'll soon see the pleasure you can give with your fingers. Don't rush yourself and don't allow yourself to be rushed. Progress inch by inch and day by day.

Tips for Putting Some Sparkle into Your Love Life

1. Read a saucy book together. Maybe try taking turns to read it out loud to one another
2. Buy and read an illustrated 'girlie' magazine together
3. Plan a candlelit dinner and put smoochy music on the record player
4. Make love out of doors
5. Make love somewhere completely different – on the sofa, on the kitchen floor, or on the dining table
6. Take a bath or a shower together
7. Look through the positions in this book and try something you've never tried before
8. Give each other a massage
9. Take a bottle of champagne to bed
10. If you normally make love with the light on try making love in the dark, and vice versa

Chapter 4

 Positional
Play

The Missionary Position

Of all the different positions a man and a woman can get into to have sex this is undoubtedly the best known and most widely used. It got its name many years ago when a group of white missionaries visited the South Sea Islands in the south west Pacific. The islanders favoured a position in which the man squatted while his partner, lying on her back, wriggled her thighs over his and then impaled herself upon his erect penis. When they caught a glimpse of two of the missionaries making love with a woman lying flat on her back and her husband lying on top of her, they were both amused and bemused.

Despite the low opinions of the islanders, this position really is an excellent way to make love. If it wasn't, it wouldn't be a perennial favourite among most couples. The first advantage this position has is that it is extremely easy to get into. She lies down, usually with her legs apart, and he lies on top of her with his legs inside hers. If a couple are of a roughly similar height they will be perfectly positioned. He will be able to slide his erect penis into her vagina and they will be able to kiss and hold one another too.

Feminists and women who play an active part in the women's liberation movement don't approve of this position. They regard it as putting a woman into an inferior and submissive position. Some claim that since the man is on top and the woman's freedom is restricted, the missionary position is a physical metaphor for modern society.

Despite this there is little doubt that huge numbers of women prefer this position to any other.

Some, but certainly not all, of the women who prefer the missionary position are passive – the sort of women who like to be told what to do, who like to be controlled by a strong male and who like to be protected and taken care of. These women like their man to make all the moves, to decide when they are going to have sex and to determine the pattern of movement during intercourse. They like him to decide the tempo and the amount of force he's going to use. They like to lie fairly still and feel that they are being made love to. All this is easy in the basic missionary position. The woman is enclosed from all sides, she has to take much of his weight on her body and unless she makes a real effort her ability to move is strictly limited. It's easy under these circumstances for a woman to feel that she has no control over what is happening to her. Women who tend to feel guilty if they enjoy sex like the missionary position because they can enjoy the physical sensations without feeling they can be criticized for being too active. For them the missionary position is pretty close to rape – and they may even heighten their pleasure if they pretend to struggle and protest a little.

The passive woman who likes the missionary position will, when she reaches her climax, probably have a number of small orgasms rather than one big one. And afterwards she'll probably like to curl up into the foetal position and clutch a pillow or soft toy to her before she falls asleep.

Not all women who like the missionary position are like this. Despite the claims made by the feminists, the missionary position is not necessarily submissive. Women can set the pace and respond very actively in this position. By spreading her legs wide a woman can move her hips and her pelvis. If she keeps her feet flat on the bed and bends her knees she will be able to meet her partner thrust for thrust. His hands are usually occupied in taking some of his weight but hers are free to hold, caress and scratch his body. She can reach his back and his buttocks easily and by pushing a hand between their bodies she can touch his penis or her own clitoris.

Many women who enjoy taking a dominant role in sex and who also like other positions have a great affection for the missionary position because they find that it provides their clitoris with the sort of stimulation necessary for an orgasm.

There is one other thing about the missionary position that

women often like: it's one of the few positions in which both partners can look directly into one another's eyes while making love, can kiss and can feel extremely close to one another. In the missionary position the two lovers are as close as they possibly can be. Human beings are the only species to have sex looking at one another (animals do it in the rear entry position) and whether they prefer to take a passive – or an active role many women get a very special type of emotional pleasure out of this position.

Those are the reasons that many women like the missionary position. What about men? Well, to some extent there is no doubt that some men like it because it fits their self-image. Just as many women are brought up to feel that they should be dependent, sensitive and submissive, so many men are taught that they should be dominant, aggressive, competitive and independent. They feel happiest when they are in a controlling position. The missionary position makes them feel masculine. As a general rule, men who have doubts about their masculinity do not like positions in which a woman takes an aggressive, dominating role and so for them the missionary position is perfect.

But there is also no doubt that many men like the missionary position for the same reason that many women do – it's one of the few positions in which both partners can kiss while they make love, can feel the warmth of each other's bodies and can look into each other's eyes. Finally, there is no doubt that men like the missionary position because it is, for them, an extremely stimulating position. Unlike some positions it isn't usually difficult for a man to reach an orgasm in this position.

The basic missionary position is just the start. There are many possible variations, most of which are fairly easy to get into. Below I've listed the primary variations and described their advantages. Some of these positions have developed away from the basic missionary position – and may, indeed, incorporate features of other positions such as 'woman on top'.

 Variation 1

The most common variation on the missionary position is called *flanquette* by the French. The basic difference is that instead of having both his legs between her thighs the man has one leg outside her thighs and the other inside. The main advantage of this variation is that there is extra contact between the penis and the clitoris – with the result that women usually find it easier to reach an orgasm. The other advantage is that both partners usually find it easier to move. She tends to have one hip lifted slightly off the bed and can move her pelvis more freely. He may be able to take most of his weight on one side, giving him a chance to use one hand to caress her body.

Variation 2

Strictly speaking, you could argue about whether or not this is a variation. The only difference to the ordinary missionary position is that she slips a pillow under her bottom. This changes the position of her pelvis and may make it easier for her to have an orgasm. If she is especially slim or has rather small buttocks the pillow will also make the position far more comfortable.

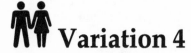

Variation 3

Many of the variations on the basic missionary position involve a fair amount of movement by one partner or the other. In this variation she lies flat on her back to start with while he moves into a kneeling position between her legs. He then puts both his hands underneath her buttocks and lifts her up off the bed. She wraps her legs around his waist. He then manoeuvers himself into a position where he can enter her. Neither partner has much freedom in this position and there is virtually no opportunity for fondling, holding or kissing. He has a good view of what is going on and has more or less total control.

Variation 4

She lies flat on her back and lifts her legs straight up into the air so that her feet are pointing at the ceiling. He then kneels and moves as close to her as he can and she lowers her legs onto his shoulders. Both partners can see one another but there is relatively little skin contact in this position. He can't fondle her because he has to hold her to him and unless she has very long arms she won't be able to fondle him. He is in total control. The main advantage of this position is that it is possible for him to penetrate her very deeply and get his penis a long way inside her. Some men like this position because it makes them feel aggressive and powerful. Some women like it because they enjoy the sense of deep penetration and because it is very much a position that emphasizes male strength.

Variation 5

She lies on her back with her legs lying flat on the bed and her knees fairly wide apart. He then kneels with one knee between her legs and the other knee outside her legs. He then lifts her up and pulls her onto him. Because of the slightly different angle this position may stimulate the clitoris more than other more 'straight on' positions.

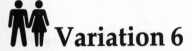 **Variation 6**

In some positions the only parts of the two bodies that touch are the parts that have to touch if they're going to have sex. This is one of them. She lies on her back with her legs raised straight up into the air. He then wriggles into a position so that he is lying at right angles to her. Unless the bed is unusually wide his head will be sticking over one side and his feet will be sticking over the other so this variation is probably best tried on the floor. Neither can really see one another although either of them can touch her clitoris while they make love. I really can't think of any specific advantage with this position. It's something to be tried on a wet Sunday afternoon when you've tried everything else.

 **Variation 7**

This time he is the first to lie down flat on his back. She then lies down with her head facing in the opposite direction. (Lots of room is needed for this position.) He parts his legs slightly and she moves towards him, putting her legs over his thighs. They then wriggle together, push his erect penis down and try to insert it into her vagina. Neither partner can see the other and there is very little skin contact. His penis will probably press hard against the upper wall of her vagina and will stimulate her clitoris.

Variation 8

This is a position for arm-wrestling champions. Unless both of you can do at least fifty press-ups I don't recommend it. To begin with he lies face down. He then lifts himself up on outstretched arms, keeping his knees, ankles and feet on the floor. She then lies on her back and wriggles underneath him, putting her feet on the floor near to his calves. She then puts her arms around him and pulls herself up to him so that only her feet remain on the floor. Her pelvis should by now be in roughly the right position for them to have intercourse. Since it is relatively rare for a penis to be able to find its way into a vagina without a little help she will probably have to let go with one hand for a moment while she impales herself upon him. It's a position that will probably result in at least one failed attempt so don't try it unless you're both prepared to collapse in a fit of giggles. Once you're in position all four arms will be totally immobilized. Neither partner can see what is going on but if you're lucky you may be able to snatch a kiss or two. I'm tempted to dub this position 'the contraceptive variation' since I suspect that very few babies have been conceived this way.

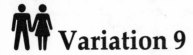 Variation 9

This is another version of the missionary position that seems to have developed quite a long way. It could equally well be considered a variation on 'woman astride'. He sits on a table or on the edge of the bed and she then scrambles up so that she is squatting on his lap with her arms around his neck. She then stretches out her legs behind him, lowers herself so that she is impaled on his penis and lowers the upper part of her body. He holds her and she takes her arms from around his neck. To complete the position the two of them interlock hands and wrists so that he is supporting her weight and she is stretched out with her body horizontal to the floor.

 Variation 10

In most of the variations on the missionary position at least one partner is mostly horizontal. But both partners can be vertical. She will probably have to lean against a wall if she isn't going to fall over. He then stands in front of her with his legs inside hers. She is pinned against the wall but they are close to one another, can kiss and can touch one another. Unlike the basic missionary position both of them can use their hands. If there is no wall or tree available it is possible to have sex this way as long as both partners have their legs spread slightly for stability. Women (or, indeed, men) who are shorter than their partners will need to stand on a couple of thick telephone directories or a couple of house bricks. If there is a dramatic difference in height a set of stairs may make this position more tenable. The taller partner stands on the lower step. This position is useful when out of doors, acting spontaneously, as no preparation or equipment and relatively little privacy are needed. Another advantage is that it is possible to make a quick getaway.

There are several possible variations on this variation. The most obvious (unsuitable for shop doorways and other external venues) involves her wrapping both her legs around his waist and being held in his arms. This is really a 'fun' alternative since neither partner is likely to have an orgasm. Finally, if he holds her legs it is possible to practise oral sex in an upside-down vertical position. A crash helmet is an optional but advisable extra for her in this position.

The Woman on Top Position

In the basic woman on top or woman astride position the male partner lies flat on his back and the woman kneels above him, lowering herself down onto him from above. This position, which used to be especially popular in Ancient Greece and has always been very popular in China and Japan, is the most aggressive and assertive position a woman can adopt and the most passive for the man. It's also known, rather colourfully, as 'riding St George'.

There are advantages for both partners. It gives her a unique opportunity to control the depth to which his penis penetrates her and it gives her a chance to control the speed and rhythm of their love-making. She can lean forwards, kiss him and dangle her breasts in front of his face. Or she can lean backwards and hold herself out of reach. She can grip his wrists and stop him from moving or she can allow him to fondle her breasts. She can reach down and touch his penis or she can help herself to orgasm manually. She can see him enter her and can allow him to watch. If she leans back she will be able to stimulate her clitoris and keep herself close to orgasm for long periods of time. She can either move up and down or round and round or from side to side. (When a woman in this position moves from side to side the French call it 'travelling on the Lyon mail coach'.)

Women who like to remain in control, who are frightened of being dominated or who want to assert themselves like this position. If their lover is older or has been ill the woman on top position enables them to do most of the work. Many women claim that they get more orgasms in this position, particularly if they are feeling especially aggressive.

As far as he is concerned, being the passive partner may be something of an experiment or an adventure. It is one of the few positions where he can watch her as she approaches orgasm and one of the few positions in which he can touch, kiss, suck and play with her breasts and nipples. Men usually find that they need a good erection in order to enter a woman in this position but once they are inside intercourse is likely to be prolonged. Men who suffer from premature ejaculation often find this position useful.

Some lovers make love in this position to start with then, when she has had her orgasm they revert to the missionary position. This gives a man a chance to have his orgasm and women who have had a climax like the chance to touch and hold their partner. Using these two positions in this way helps to avoid the dissent which can occur if he has a tendency to fall asleep the moment he has had his orgasm.

There are a number of variations on the basic woman on top position. It's worth remembering that, because this basic position has always been popular in the East, some of the variations are best suited to individuals who are small and agile. Larger Western couples may find some of these positions painful or impossible.

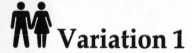 **Variation 1**

The first and most obvious variation is for her to face away from him. This means that they can't see one another and can't kiss. He can't really see what is happening and certainly can't see or touch her breasts unless he levers himself into a half-sitting position and puts a hand round in front of her. Women have even more control than usual when facing the 'wrong' direction. They are also free to play with his scrotum and testicles. As with the more normal face to face position they can control the stimulation on the clitoris by leaning forwards and backwards.

Variation 2

For this variation he kneels and then leans back with one or both hands behind him. Facing him, she then shuffles her bottom in between his thighs so that she can impale herself on his penis. Her legs can be draped over his knees. She has to stretch her hands out behind her to stop herself from falling backwards so neither of them can use their hands very much and there is relatively little skin contact. They can, however, both see one another and both have a wonderful view of what is going on. Since she is still on top of him she still has control.

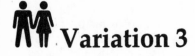

Variation 3

He lies on his back and she sits astride him as before. The only difference is that she has both legs on the same side and is sitting 'side-saddle'. She'll probably need to balance herself by putting her arms behind her and taking some of her weight on her hands which are on the floor (or bed) on the other side of his legs.

Variation 4

He kneels and sits straight up. She goes down into a squatting position with her thighs parallel to the ground, balancing on the balls of her feet and holding onto him with her hands. He puts his hands under her bottom to help steady her. She lowers herself onto him, opening her thighs so that she can get close enough to him. She can keep one hand free so that she can fondle him and he can reach round and caress her bottom. Since both partners are vertical from the waist up there can be quite a lot of skin contact with this position. She has almost total control over what happens.

Variation 5

For this one he lies on his side and lifts one leg up into the air. She then kneels astride his lower leg and, again, lowers herself onto him. She holds his upper leg so that it is pointing more or less straight up into the air. She is in control and he is very much in her hands. He needs to be fairly agile to manage this position.

Variation 6

If she can get into the traditional meditative lotus position (with her legs crossed and tucked under her) she can sit on top of him while he lies flat on his back on the floor. She can try this position either facing him or facing away from him. He will be supporting all her weight on one small part of his body, but if she was big enough and heavy enough to hurt him she probably wouldn't be able to get into the lotus position in the first place.

Variation 7

This position is only suitable for trained athletes or people who are not frightened to laugh at themselves. He lies flat on his back and lifts his knees and his bottom off the floor. He opens his legs and she backs towards him in a squatting position, her upper body more or less parallel to the floor and her hands on the floor. Folded over she then backs onto his penis. Neither partner can see the other, both are balancing in rather uncomfortable positions and neither can use their hands. The only point of contact is genital. You'll probably wonder why you're bothering.

Variation 8

He lies flat on his back then lifts his bottom off the floor an inch or so by lifting himself upon his outstretched arms. She squats, facing away from him, and backs towards him until his penis enters her vagina. This is similar to Variation 7 except that his legs are still on the floor. It is possible to get quite deep penetration in this position but there is a lot of strain on his back and she probably won't find it very comfortable. Both of them have to work hard to keep his penis inside her.

 Variation 9

He sits with his legs apart. Facing him she edges forward and puts her legs around his body. She then sits down onto his erect penis. They can hold one another as tightly as they wish and hold each other up. There can be plenty of skin contact and they can kiss and fondle one another.

Variation 10

An ordinary upright dining chair is needed. He sits on it. Facing him she then sits astride him. That's all there is to it. It's marvellously simple and an excellent position since both partners can touch, caress and kiss one another. It's a good position for him if he easily gets tired and it requires little effort on her part. Their bodies are close and there is plenty of skin contact. She has to do most of the work and penetration is not too deep.

Variation 11

A small low table is needed. He lies flat on his back on the table. With one leg either side of both him and the table she either backs onto his penis or moves forward onto it. Unless the table is fairly long he may find this uncomfortable. If she has arthritis or joint troubles of any kind she will find this position easy to get into.

With a little ingenuity, a little patience and a lot of agility it is possible to devise many other variations on the basic woman on top position.

The Rear Entry Position

The basic rear entry position is very popular and is one of the most natural of all. For most mammals it is the only option. Many men and women claim that this position gives them more satisfaction than any other.

The position is as easy to describe as it is to try. The woman kneels down and supports her shoulders by putting her hands on the floor. Her back should be horizontal to the floor. The man approaches her from behind and uses a hand to guide his penis into her vagina. He will usually be in a kneeling position but he can also try squatting. She has no control and unless she looks over her shoulder she can see nothing of what is happening. He, however, can see everything. He can fondle or slap her buttocks and, by turning his body slightly to one side, he can

see her breasts hanging down underneath her. If he leans forward he will be able to touch her breasts and her nipples. He will also be able to reach round and touch her clitoris. It is possible for him to penetrate her very deeply from this position. He can get maximum penetration by sitting astride her body, like a jockey on a horse and gripping her with his thighs. In any rear entry position it is important that he does not penetrate too far or push too hard since it is possible for him to hit an ovary – which can be exceedingly painful.

If she finds this position tiring a pile of cushions or pillows can be built up underneath her as support. Alternatively she can kneel on the floor with her chest resting on a bed or chair. The lower her head the deeper he will be able to penetrate her. With her head resting on a chair or bed he can hold her hands behind her back in a very submissive position.

For men this is one of the most aggressive of all positions. It is widely used by Eskimos where the lack of face to face contact is considered an advantage in a society where men commonly loan out their wives to honoured guests. Men who like to dominate, who like to initiate sexual activity and who prefer to keep some emotional distance usually prefer this position to any other.

Most women would agree that for them this is the most submissive and most impersonal of positions. A woman can't see her partner and she has little or no control over what happens. Women who like to take a subsidiary role, or who like to maintain an emotional distance, often prefer this position to any other.

The standard rear entry position is sometimes known by the French term of *croupade*. There are, as you might expect, a number of possible variations.

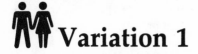 **Variation 1**

In the most common rear entry variation, she lies on her side and he, also lying on his side, approaches her from behind. Far from being aggressive, this variation is one of the gentlest ways to make love and it is particularly suitable for partners who may be ill or convalescent. It is for obvious reasons especially useful for pregnant women. Men who can only get weak erections will find that this position enables them to enter their partner very easily, while many men who have suffered from partial impotence have regained their lost confidence using it. The position is also very useful if either partner is overweight or, indeed, if both are overweight. He can reach round and touch her breasts or clitoris.

👫 Variation 2

She lies face downwards on the floor. He then approaches her from one side, putting just one leg between hers. This is the reverse of the frontal *flanquette* position and is known by the French as *cuissade*.

👫 Variation 3

In a slightly more aggressive version of Variation 1 she lies on her side and he puts both his legs in between hers. She then lifts her upper leg, swings it round and curls it around the back of his thighs. The movement means that he can see as well as fondle her breasts.

👫 Variation 4

In a position sometimes known as T-square he lies on his side and she then backs her bottom towards his penis. Her feet are up by his face and her body is at right angles to her own legs and to his body. There is very little visual or manual contact in this position.

👫 Variation 5

She kneels in the standard rear entry position but instead of kneeling behind her he, while standing, bends down and picks up her legs. He then gets into what schoolchildren would call a wheelbarrow position. She supports her upper body on her outstretched arms and he holds her legs. He then pushes himself forward slightly so that his penis enters her. It is possible to get quite deep penetration with this position but there isn't much emotional contact and there isn't any opportunity for either partner to caress the other. A variation on this position is for her to support her upper body on a bed or comfortable chair while he holds her legs up and approaches her from behind.

 # Variation 6

Only lovers who want really deep penetration should try this one – and it's advisable to try it gently. She lies flat on her back on the floor and then lifts her legs so that they almost touch the floor beyond her head. She's coiled with her bottom and her vagina very clearly exposed.

Facing away from her he then lowers himself into a sitting position and pushes his penis into her. This is one of the most detached of all positions since neither partner can even see the other. If both partners are especially agile he can then slowly move forwards further and further, eventually supporting himself on his arms while still keeping his penis inside her vagina.

 # Variation 7

He kneels and then falls back to support himself with his arms behind him. She kneels and faces the same way that he is facing. Keeping her legs apart she then backs towards him. Her legs go outside his knees and her vagina eventually meets his penis. This is a mixture of the standard rear entry position and several of the variations on the woman on top position.

 # Variation 8

She lies on her side and pulls her knees up towards her chest. He then approaches her at right angles. Apart from the fact that he is inside her there is little physical contact with this position and there are no opportunities for holding, caressing or kissing.

# Variation 9

In a variation of the wheelbarrow position (see Variation 5) she lies with her chest and head on a table. He then approaches her from behind, lifts her legs up and holds them outstretched. Standing, he enters her from behind with her legs on each side of his body.

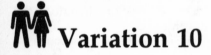# Variation 10

She stands about a yard away from a wall and leans forward, supporting her head and her arms on the wall. She has her legs wide apart. Standing, he then approaches her from behind.

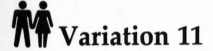# Variation 11

He leans with this back against a wall and his feet about a yard away from it (perhaps a little more or less, depending on his height). She then backs onto him. This is the only rear entry position in which the woman is in control and can decide how much movement there is and how deep he penetrates her. (It's possible to argue that this is more a variation on the woman on top position than the rear entry position.) There is quite a lot of skin contact in this position and both partners can fondle each other. She can reach behind her to touch him and he can easily reach round her to caress her breasts and her clitoris.

The Side By Side Position

Making love side by side is the least common but the most democratic of all positions. Facing one another each partner has a hand free to caress the other, there is maximum skin contact because both pairs of legs have to be entwined to make entry possible, there is emotional intimacy and control is shared so no one is dominant and no one is submissive.

The basic side by side position is peaceful, restful and physically undemanding. There are no genuine variations on this simple position.

Oral Sex

A few generations ago oral sex was probably considered to be a rather exotic sexual variation. Some would have regarded it as a perversion. Today oral sex is widely accepted as a natural, healthy and enjoyable practice. There is nothing abnormal, unhealthy or dangerous about it. Oral sex involving a mouth and the female sexual organs is known as cunnilingus. Oral sex involving a mouth and the male sexual organ is known as fellatio.

The mouth is exceptionally well designed for sexual pleasure; it is less flexible than a hand but capable of a broad range of activities. The shape of the mouth, the lips and the tongue mean that the whole structure can be used to stroke, kiss, lick, probe and penetrate the target organ. A mouth can be used gently or fiercely without there being any real risk of damage and although the partner on the receiving end undoubtedly receives the greatest amount of pleasure the partner who owns the mouth which is doing the work will often obtain a great deal of satisfaction too. Not only is the mouth well equipped with nerve endings it is also able to taste the uniquely flavoured juices that emerge from a vagina or penis.

Most traditional sex manuals discuss position 69 in which both partners perform oral sex simultaneously. The advantage of this position is that it offers both partners an equal chance to enjoy what is going on. The drawback is that it can be difficult to concentrate on what you are doing when you are approaching an orgasm. Position 69 can lead to some very frustrating experiences.

The other disadvantage with position 69 is that unless both partners are very flexible it can be quite uncomfortable. It's difficult to enjoy sex properly with cramp in one leg and a pain in the back, and it can be tricky to find a position that is equally satisfying for both partners. But if both are agile, and lucky, then position 69 can be tremendously exciting. Smelling, tasting and swallowing each other at the same moment can be an exhilarating experience.

However, it's usually easier to take turns at enjoying oral sex. With old-fashioned gallantry I suggest that she take her pleasure first. This will give him a chance to develop a really good erection. Another advantage is that women usually stay in the mood for a little while after they've had an orgasm; men on the other hand are prone to fall asleep.

I should perhaps point out that despite the fact that oral sex is now extremely popular there are still some people – women more than men – who are frightened at the prospect. She might worry about having his penis in her mouth; she may be frightened that she's going to choke; she may be alarmed at the prospect of him ejaculating inside her mouth.

If one partner is shy or reluctant to experiment then its important that the other partner doesn't push things along too quickly. There can be powerful cultural, personal and psychological factors to overcome.

The first time, he or she can begin with a simple genital kiss, keeping lips closed. He or she will probably notice that the kiss gives his or her partner great pleasure. It's best not to progress too fast, but to experiment a little more each time. If the recipient is shy, embarrassed or nervous, she or he can always indicate when to stop.

Although it is traditionally thought that the person doing the sucking or kissing is adopting the passive or submissive role, the fact is that either partner can be dominant. For example, when a woman is performing fellatio on a man, he will often be standing, sitting or lying quite still. She will be the active one, using her mouth, her head, her shoulders and her hands. Perhaps because of the slightly taboo nature of the act, when an inactive partner watches an active partner he or she may *feel* dominant. Women who really don't like performing oral sex and who do it as a favour say that they feel they are being used and that they are submitting to something indecent. But women who really enjoy fellatio will argue that they are asserting themselves sexually, and that they feel dominant.

 Cunnilingus

Finding a good position is an essential start to enjoying cunnilingus. Here are five positions which should suit both partners:

1. She sits on an ordinary chair. He kneels or squats in front of her. She then wriggles to the front of the chair so that her vagina is exposed and close to his face
2. He lies on his back on the floor or on a bed. She then gently lowers herself down onto him until her vagina meets his mouth. If she faces his feet she can use her hands to touch and play with his penis
3. She lies on her back with her knees drawn up towards her chest. He approaches her lying on his side. If her legs tire she can lower them so that her feet touch the floor on the other side of his head
4. He sits on a chair. She lies on her back on the floor in front of him. He bends down and picks her up so that her back is resting on his knees. She moves her legs so that they are over his shoulders. By now her vagina will be close to his mouth and her head will be hanging down towards the floor. If she doesn't weigh too much and she can stand the fact that the blood will rush to her head, this is an excellent position
5. She gets into a back flip position, supporting herself on her feet and her hands and offering her vagina to him. He then kneels in front of her. This position is only really suitable for female gymnasts!

Any man who is about to perform cunnilungus should remember that although the clitoris is the most sensitive part of a woman's sexual anatomy it can also be exquisitely tender. It is often better to begin by paying attention to the *labia minora* and the entrance to the vagina. It is important to take care with teeth and make sure that fingernails are not too long. Remove any rough edges with a nail file.

He can begin slowly by gently kissing her vaginal lips with his mouth. He should run his tongue along and around the vaginal entrance. Stroking and kissing and touching will be far better received than prodding and pushing and squeezing. He can try sliding his tongue into her vagina as far as it will go. Most men find the acid taste of vaginal juices pleasant and there is no need for any woman to try to disguise her natural smells or flavours (though, of course, a wash with clean water some hours before-hand is nothing more than common courtesy).

It is best to kiss around the clitoris rather than directly on top of it, and he should not stop using his fingers. He shouldn't blow into the vagina – if he does he may force air into her peritoneal cavity and that can be dangerous.

Finally, it is worth remembering that although saliva is slight-ly spermicidal cunnilungus can, if it follows fellatio and kissing in the right order, result in a conception. Never expect a partner to practise cunnilingus if there is any infection present.

 Fellatio

Here are five positions for fellatio:

1. He sits in a chair (an easy chair or a dining chair will do). She then kneels in front of him and lowers her head into his lap
2. He stands and she kneels in front of him
3. He gets down onto the floor on all fours. She then crawls underneath him from behind, lying on her back. By moving her head up a few inches she can take him into her mouth
4. He kneels down with his thighs and back held straight. She then crouches down in front of him
5. He kneels on the floor and sits back on his haunches. She then lies on the floor in front of him with her face in his lap. She may find it easier if her body lies to the side and she curls herself up into a semi-foetal position.

When performing fellatio for the first time all women ask (or, more accurately, would like to ask) the same questions: 'Is he going to come? And if he does what do I do?'

This really is something to sort out beforehand. He should try to warn her when he's coming (with a little experience she won't need telling) and he should not be at all offended if she doesn't want him to come in her mouth.

Whether or not he does come in her mouth is all a question of taste – hers. And the same goes for whether or not she should swallow. I'm assured that semen has a rather bitter, salty taste. Some women like it, some dislike it, and many don't think that the taste is positive enough to make much of a difference as to whether he comes in their mouth or not. They think that the texture, the feel and the very fact that he has ejaculated into their mouth is enough to be dealing with.

If she likes it then there are no problems, although she should try to catch the ejaculate with her tongue. Women have choked to death when men have ejaculated into their lungs (though this is a very rare occurrence). If she doesn't like the taste but she wants him to come in her mouth then she could experiment with a deep throat or deep mouth technique, if she's prepared to swallow. In a deep throat technique, she takes his penis right into her throat and he ejaculates straight into her stomach. This is a trick rather akin to sword swallowing, and very few women master it; it takes a good deal of practice. In a deep mouth technique, she takes his penis right into the back of her mouth so that the semen spends very little time in her mouth before disappearing down into her stomach. If a woman doesn't want to swallow for any reason (and since you ask, semen is nutritionally valuable but contains very few calories – about five to the teaspoonful; you'd have to swallow a lot for it to make any difference to a slimming diet) but she wants him to come in her mouth then she might like to have a handkerchief ready as rushing out to the bathroom or aiming at a spittoon tend to ruin the atmosphere.

If she doesn't want him to come in her mouth at all then he should respect this wish and make sure that he pulls out of her mouth in time. He should also try to give her some appropriate warning. Even if she doesn't want him to come in her mouth she may like him to ejaculate into her hands or onto or in between her breasts.

There is, of course, one other important question women ask and that is: 'What am I supposed to do?'

The answer is simple. Begin by kissing the shaft and then the tip of his penis. You will find that the underside of the glans is the most sensitive part. His testicles will also be sensitive to your lips and tongue. Do not blow (despite the fact that fellatio is often known as a 'blow job') nor suck as though you were trying to drink a soft drink through a straw. Moisten his penis with your tongue and lick it as you would lick an ice cream. Then slip your lips around the glans of his penis and lower your head a little, don't forget to use your hands. Move your head up and down slowly, and move your tongue around his penis. From this point on, only practise will make you better.

Finally, it should go without saying that a man who expects his partner to perform oral sex should make sure that he washes the entire area thoroughly beforehand. Men who are uncircumsized should roll down their foreskins and clean underneath. Don't be tempted to use perfumes of any kind. The most enticing smell is the natural male smell. Never expect a partner to practise fellatio if there is any infection present.

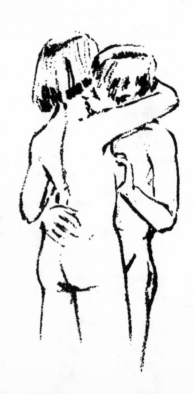

Masturbation

The hand is a wonderful creation. It can be gentle or strong. It can manipulate, caress, stroke, tickle or grasp. It is flexible. It can be used as a substitute penis or a replacement vagina. It can directly and specifically stimulate parts of the human body in ways that ordinary sex rarely stimulates.

Most people begin their sex lives by learning to masturbate. It used to be thought that masturbation was an exclusively male habit. It isn't. As the results of my survey show (on pages 32 to 38) masturbation is common among women too. But masturbation need not be a lonely occupation. There are many times when it can be delightful to masturbate a partner to orgasm. Unlike a mechanical vibrator a hand is sensitive. It can feel what it touches and provide feedback to its owner. If two partners masturbate one another simultaneously they will double their pleasure.

It's important to remember too that masturbation can be used to help bring a partner to climax when he or, more commonly, she has failed to reach an orgasm through intercourse. Many women and many men feel guilty if she cannot have an orgasm when his penis is inside her. But in fact most of the time most women can't. They need extra stimulation; they need outside help.

Masturbation can be used as an alternative to sex, a preparation for the real thing or to help one or both partners achieve an orgasm after sex.

Strangely, many men and women who are broadminded about other aspects of sex still feel shy or embarrassed or guilty about masturbation. They find it difficult to ask a partner to help them to reach a climax and they feel unable to explain what they want or what would please them most.

Try not to allow these feelings to inhibit you. Talk to one another or, if you don't want to talk, then show him, or her, precisely what you want by moving his (or her) fingers a little in this direction and then a little in that direction. If you want him, or her, to press a little harder, use your fingers to press down and show him or her what you want.

👫 Notes for him masturbating her

Be gentle. Don't aim straight for the clitoris. Most men don't like the end of their penis being grabbed; the clitoris is similarly packed with nerve endings and is just as sensitive as the most sensitive part of the male organ. Start slow and soft. Touch the outer part of her vagina. Touch the pubic hair-covered *mons*. Move your fingers from side to side. Start with a whole hand massage and gradually begin to concentrate on one or two fingers as you find out what she wants. Experiment. Communicate. Ask her what she wants. Build up the pressure and the speed slowly and carefully. Use the flat of your hand on her vulva, gently push your middle finger in between her vaginal lips. Move the tip of your finger in and out of her. Press the ball of your hand just above the pubis. Gently stretch her vaginal lips. Use both hands if you can. Switch to your tongue occasionally.

If she is dry dip your fingers in your mouth and moisten her with your saliva. If your hands are at all rough use a baby oil or a plain hand cream. Make sure that your fingernails are cut short and that there are no ragged edges. Push a whole finger into her vagina if she likes that. Or more. Press upwards onto the upper vaginal wall. With one hand concentrating on her vagina use your other to concentrate on the area around her clitoris. But still keep away from the clitoris itself. Remember that gentle rubbing and pulling on the skin around the clitoris will result in the clitoris itself being pulled. If you get close and then lose her it may be because you moved in the wrong direction at a critical moment. With time you'll get to know when she's coming. Ask her to tell you what she wants.

♟ Notes for her masturbating him

Begin with your fingernails on the skin around his penis. Drag your nails along the skin of his scrotum and gently hold his scrotum in your fingers. Try touching the skin between his scrotum and his anus. Gently run your fingers up and down the shaft of his penis. Hold his penis carefully between your fingers then move your fingers up and down. Ask him if he wants you to hold him tighter – or not so tightly. You may need a lubricant. Baby oil is good; saliva will do perfectly well. Speed up or slow down to build up and reduce the suspense. If he has a foreskin pull it back. Grip his penis either with your thumb and first finger or with the whole of your hand. Change hands if you get tired. Don't be shy about watching when he ejaculates – he's unlikely to mind, indeed he'll probably find it an extra turn-on.

Anal Sex

Although anal sex is illegal in many parts of the world (in Britain and in parts of America for example) it is remarkably popular among heterosexuals. One of the world's biggest sex surveys showed that more than half of all heterosexuals in America have experienced anal stimulation (with a finger or vibrator) or actual anal intercourse and 10 per cent of heterosexual couples regularly have anal sex.

Thousands of years ago anal sex was widely used because it allowed participants to avoid any risk of conception. Today the spread of AIDS in large parts of Africa can be explained by the fact that anal intercourse is still used for this reason. These days, however, most of the people who practise anal sex do so because they enjoy it as a variation on the more usual themes. Some women find that anal intercourse gives them a more intense orgasm while some men claim that penetrating a tight anal sphincter gives them a special type of pleasure.

There are, I must warn you, some hazards associated with anal intercourse:

1. Anal intercourse is often painful, particularly the first time. It is likely to be especially painful if the passive partner (usually but not always the woman, since some women do penetrate their male partners with vibrators) has piles or any other anal condition
2. If the active partner pushes too hard or is impatient it is possible to damage the tissues
3. Infection is a real risk if anal and vaginal intercourse are mixed. Some partners find it exciting to alternate between the two entrances. There is a risk that bacteria from the intestinal tract may be introduced into the vagina. Long-term infections can result. To avoid this problem, or rather to minimize the risk, vaginal intercourse should not follow anal intercourse unless and until the penis has been cleaned. Wearing a condom while practising anal intercourse does, of course, help to minimize the risk of infection.
4. AIDS experts now claim that the only heterosexual activity known to result in the spread of AIDS is receptive anal intercourse. This means that if you have anal intercourse

with occasional sex partners then there must be a risk that you will catch AIDS. If you have anal sex with one regular partner and you are both faithful to one another and neither of you are HIV positive then you will not catch AIDS. There is more information about AIDS on page 188.

5. Regular anal intercourse over a long period of time could lead to a stretching of the anal sphincter. This could then lead to the development of incontinence.

With all these hazards why do so many people try anal intercourse?

There are, I suspect, three main reasons.

First, any sexual act which breaks a long-established taboo is regarded as exciting by many people. Now that oral sex is widely accepted as 'normal', having anal sex breaks one of the last remaining taboos.

Second, there is little doubt that anal sex appeals to individuals who enjoy sex games in which one partner takes a dominant role and the other takes a submissive role. Because anal intercourse is painful and is sometimes regarded as humiliating for the passive partner, this sex variation appeals to individuals who want to express psychological forces through sex.

Third, the anal region is well supplied with nerves which follow much the same pathway as the nerves supplying the penis and the vagina. Afficionados argue that anal intercourse can be sexually exciting.

If you want to try anal sex (as an active or a passive partner) you should remember that lubrication is vitally important. There is little natural lubrication around the anus and the sphincter which guards the rectum is very tight. The partner who intends to do the penetration (either with a penis or a vibrator) should apply plenty of lubrication. A water-soluble gel is excellent but in the absence of anything else saliva will do fine.

Then, gently try pushing a fingertip into the anus. Press very gently. As pressure is applied from the outside so the passive partner, the partner being penetrated, should bear down on the finger. It may help deliberately to tighten up the anal sphincter and then to let it relax.

Various positions are suitable for anal intercourse. Any of the rear entry positions will do but the standard rear entry position is probably most popular. So, once the anal sphincter has been opened a little with a fingertip, a larger object – a penis or small vibrator – can be tried. Remember that large quantities of lubrication will be essential. The anal sphincter normally closes automatically when any object approaches from outside so the active partner will need a considerable amount of determination to overcome this natural barrier. The passive partner must be able to relax.

Unless at least one of you is experienced you are unlikely to be able to penetrate more than an inch or so on your first attempts at anal intercourse. It is perfectly possible for both partners to reach an orgasm in this position.

Variations on the Theme

It is possible to have a type of intercourse without using either the vagina or the anus. Some couples use these variations to avoid conception or when infection or menstruation makes ordinary intercourse impossible, impractical or unacceptable.

Here are four variations on the more traditional themes.

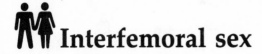 Interfemoral sex

This variation is widely used by prostitutes (especially transvestite male prostitutes). She holds her thighs together tightly and he pushes his penis in between them. The standard rear entry positions are most suitable although it is possible to penetrate from the front. She mustn't move too much or else there will not be enough friction. Interfemoral sex is sometimes used as a type of foreplay by some couples.

Intermammillary sex

If her breasts are large enough to be squeezed together to make a vagina-like channel then intermammillary intercourse will be possible. One of the best positions is for her to lie flat on her back and hold her breasts together. He he kneels over her and places his penis in between her breasts, while she is squeezing her breasts together. One advantage of this variation is that both partners can watch the moment of ejaculation. If she wants to take a more passive role then he can mould her breasts around his penis. Remember that when leaving a penis semen may travel several feet.

 Gluteal sex

The crease between the mound of her buttocks can be used as a vaginal alternative. This can be done in several positions. She can kneel, in the rear entry position. He can lie underneath her, with her facing upwards. Or they can stand together both facing in the same direction. If she contracts her gluteal muscles and rotates her pelvis and he thrusts then he should be able to reach an orgasm this way.

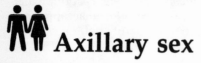 Axillary sex

A suitably damp, cavernous and hairy part of a woman's body is her armpit. Some men and a few women find axillary sex very exciting, others find the whole idea bizarre. It's difficult to describe positions in which he can insert his penis into her armpit, but if you're really keen you shouldn't have too much difficulty in working out what to do. He usually has to do most of the work though she may be able to help by moving her shoulder and upper arm.

Finding the Right Position

There are hundreds of different ways for a man and a woman to have sex together. Some of them are bizarre and unlikely to be used except by couples who are keen to work their way through the full range of physical possibilities. Other positions are popular because they satisfy particular needs.

Some positions lend themselves better than others to certain types of movement. He may like to push hard, thrusting deep into her. She may like to rock from side to side as he thrusts or grind her pelvis round in a circle. He may like to make small rapid movements or long slow ones. Different positions suit these different movements and require one or other partner to take control. When she is on top, for example, she will find it far easier to rotate her pelvis than when they are in the missionary position. When they are in the missionary position he will find that he has a considerable amount of control over how deep his penis enters her. If she puts her legs over his shoulders, he will be able to thrust himself deep into her body. If, in the missionary position with her lying flat, she flexes her knees and lifts her legs a little then she will be able to thrust back; either of them will be able to select the rhythm.

When she sits astride him she will be able to control the speed and the depth to which his penis enters her and she will have far more say over the way her clitoris is stimulated. Men may find that in this position the stimulus on the penis is less intense – this means that the woman astride or woman on top position is often particularly useful for men who ejaculate prematurely or for couples who want to prolong intercourse. When he wants to come he may need to take more control over the speed and depth of thrust, or he may need to change to another position.

There are many things to bear in mind when choosing a new position to try. Here I have listed the twenty most common limitations and requirements and in the table on page 97 have suggested the position most likely to suit.

1. Physical deformities
If he has bad arthritis in his knees or if she suffers from backache then the range of suitable positions will be restricted. There is no point at all in trying a position which is bound to be painful.

2. Weight

If he is very much heavier than she is then woman on top positions will probably be more acceptable. The missionary position and its variations can be extremely uncomfortable if he is much bigger than her.

3. Pregnancy

I deal with sex in pregnancy at greater length on page 154 but I think it is worth pointing out that rear entry positions, side by side positions and woman on top positions are much better than the missionary position for pregnant women. It's sensible to choose positions in which little strain is put on the woman's abdomen.

4. Size of sexual organs

Positions in which deep penetration is inevitable are fairly unsuitable when he has an unusually large penis and she has an unusually small vagina. On the other hand if she has a large vagina and he has a small penis then a deep penetration position will be useful.

5. Fears and hang-ups

There is no point at all in choosing a position that appeals to one of you if the other half of your partnership is terrified by the prospect. Never try anything that both of you don't want to try.

6. Her ability to reach an orgasm

If she has great difficulty in getting pleasure out of sex – let alone reaching an orgasm – then it will be wise to choose a position in which her clitoris will receive the greatest amount of stimulation.

7. His ability to reach an orgasm or maintain a firm erection

If he has difficulty in having an orgasm – or maintaining an erection – then choose a position that helps him. Some positions need a really firm erection – others can be managed successfully with a moderately firm erection.

8. Her need to dominate

Some women need to take a dominating, aggressive role in sex. They feel uncomfortable if they can't be on top or can't be active.

9. His need to dominate

Commonly men feel uncomfortable if they aren't in a dominating position. Some men feel a real need to be aggressive during sex. Their choice of sexual position will reflect this need.

10. Her need to be dominated

Shy, diffident, complaisant women often only feel comfortable when they know that their partner is taking charge.

11. His need to be dominated

Less commonly, some men feel more comfortable when the woman they are making love to takes charge.

12. A desire to find a position that makes kissing possible

Some people – usually women – feel uncomfortable if they can't kiss their partners during sex. Without a kiss they feel that they are being used, that sex is too impersonal.

13. A desire to find a position that enables both partners to see one another

In some positions the two partners face in opposite directions. Visual contact disappears completely. Some men and women strongly dislike this type of sex.

14. A desire to find a position in which both partners can watch their sex organs

Some people are turned on by being able to see what is going on.

15. A desire to achieve maximum skin contact

Many people like to feel that they have close skin contact during sex. This makes them feel more intimate.

16. A desire to share everything equally and democratically

Many loving couples prefer positions where they can both share and enjoy all aspects of their physical relationship.

17. His need to touch and fondle her breasts

Men are often stimulated sexually by touching their partner's breasts.

18. Her need to touch her own clitoris

Many women can only reach an orgasm if they can masturbate while they have sex.

19. Both partners' desire for purely genital contact

Some men and women want to distance themselves from each other and find a position in which the main or only contact is genital.

20. Both partners' desire for prolonged intercourse

If he suffers from premature ejaculation, or they simply want a long session, then a position in which the orgasm is likely to be delayed will be popular.

Choosing the best positions for YOU

To find which sexual positions will suit you and your partner best make a list of the things you both enjoy and the things you both want out of sex, then study the chart on pages 96–97.

Most couples have two or three favourite positions. However often they try new positions they invariably return to those old, well-tried positions because they find them more satisfying either physically or emotionally. However, at different times in their lives and in different circumstances people may change their allegiance.

Here are some facts about position choice that are worth remembering:

1. Just because you start having sex in one position it doesn't mean that you have to finish in the same position. Some couples start off in a position that enables her to get an orgasm and then move to a position he prefers
2. No one position is better than any other. Whatever gives you both satisfaction and pleasure is right
3. Different positions offer different kinds of pleasure – but not necessarily different degrees of pleasure
4. Battles over things – money for example – may lead to battles in the bedroom. If he is trying to establish superiority in the living room he may try to establish superiority in the

bedroom. Couples who can compromise over a choice of sexual position can usually reach an agreement on other matters that may threaten to divide them

5. Past experience – happy or unhappy – may lead to long-lasting preferences for specific types of sexual position

6. He or she may find it difficult to accept certain positions because of long-established attitudes towards sex. For example, some men who are sensitive about their macho image may find it difficult to accept a woman on top position. And women who have been brought up to feel that a woman should take a subsidiary role during sex may also find it difficult to accept a position in which they take an aggressive role

7. By looking at your sex life – and the positions you tend to choose – it is possible to learn a lot about yourself and about your relationship with your partner(s). Analysing your favourite sexual positions may help you identify strengths and weaknesses in your relationship. For example, if you both prefer positions in which there is little physical contact it may be that you need to express your feelings for one another a little more. If she always insists on a woman on top position then maybe she is striving to dominate the relationship. If he prefers a rear entry position then maybe he is unduly aggressive

8. Sometimes an emotionally matched couple may find their sex life is difficult to organize. If she is very passive and prefers him to take a dominating, aggressive role during sex then this may produce difficulties if he is also meek and reluctant to assert himself. The answer may be to use a 'democratic' position where neither partner has to dominate the other

9. As a general rule, whatever the physical delights may be, most people try to avoid sexual positions in which they feel psychologically uncomfortable. If you're male and you don't like the woman on top position this may be a sign that you are unduly conscious of, and determined to protect, your macho image. If you're female and you find rear entry positions unacceptable then maybe you're reluctant to allow a man the chance to dominate you; or maybe you just don't like sexual positions in which there is relatively little emotional contact

(Continued on page 98)

Choosing the best position for YOU

Key to chart

A   Want close skin contact
B   Both want to watch sex organs in action
C   He wants to be able to touch and/or fondle her breasts
D   She wants to be able to masturbate herself
E   Want position where main contact is genital
F   Need a position that will help prolong intercourse
G   She is pregnant
H   He is much heavier than her
I   She is much heavier than him
J   Both want to be able to see one another
K   Want to be able to kiss one another
L   He has difficulty in obtaining a firm erection
M   She wants a position where clitoris will receive maximum
      stimulation
N   Want a position suitable for a 'quick getaway'
O   One or both partners athletic and gymnastic
P   He has unusually large penis
Q   He has unusually small penis
R   She wants to dominate
S   He wants to dominate
T   Want position where no one dominates
U   Want position where deep penetration is possible

Missionary   M
Woman on top   WOT
Rear entry   RE
Side by side   SBS
Variation   V

1	Basic M	10	MV9	19	WOT V7	28	RE V4
2	MV1	11	MV10	20	WOT V8	29	RE V5
3	MV2	12	Basic WOT	21	WOT V9	30	RE V6
4	MV3	13	WOT V1	22	WOT V10	31	RE V7
5	MV4	14	WOT V2	23	WOT V11	32	RE V8
6	MV5	15	WOT V3	24	Basic RE	33	RE V9
7	MV6	16	WOT V4	25	RE V1	24	RE V10
8	MV7	17	WOT V5	26	RE V2	35	RE V11
9	MV8	18	WOT V6	27	RE V3	36	Basic SBS

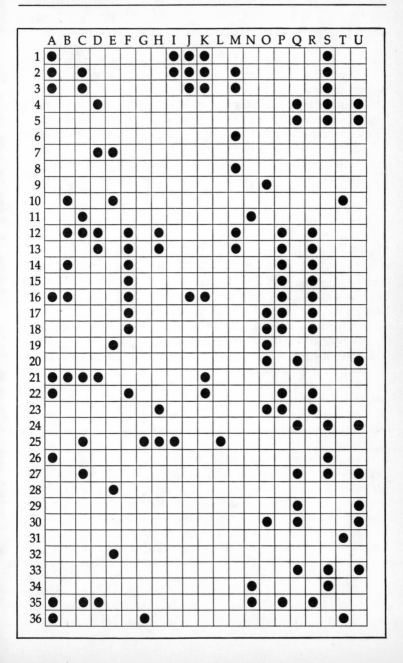

10. A change in some aspect of your life may lead to a temporary change in your favourite sexual position. For example, if he breaks a leg or she gets pregnant then different positions may have to be used. When things return to normal you'll probably revert to your old-time favourite positions
11. Couples who work their way through as many positions as possible may have a relationship that is more physical than anything else and that is based on day to day stimulation rather than long-term commitment
12. It may be possible for you to revolutionize your sex life by finding a new position which suits your psychological and physical needs more closely than anything you have tried before.

Afterplay

Once a man has ejaculated his interest in sex – and sometimes in his partner – rapidly declines. His penis will shrink and with it will go his sex drive. For a period of time which varies a lot, normally in accordance with age, he will be uninterested in sex and unable to achieve another erection.

During the arousal period a large amount of blood flows into a man's pelvic area and his muscles contract and tighten. After sex the blood is rapidly diverted away from that area and the muscles relax, with the result that excitement is replaced by drowsiness and a general feeling of lethargy. It's hardly surprising that so many men fall asleep the moment they have had an orgasm.

Women are quite different. Even when they have had an orgasm most women remain alert, sensitive and loving. Many women claim that they feel a greater need for love and reassurance and comfort and cuddling immediately after sex than at any other time in their lives. They come down from ecstasy much more slowly. They feel romantic. They often remain sexually excited. They want to be held, caressed and talked to. They want to know that their partner loves them. If their partner rolls over and falls asleep the moment after he has ejaculated they are likely to feel desperately empty and lonely, vulnerable and used. The happy, relaxed and satisfied feelings of a moment before can quickly and readily turn into disappointment, guilt, sadness and even depression.

To a certain extent the main problem – him falling asleep when she wants a cuddle – can be overcome by choosing a better time for love-making. If you only ever make love when you are both tired and ready for sleep then it will hardly be surprising if he finds it impossible to stay awake. Decide instead to make love in the early morning or during the daytime.

A woman can help too by resisting the temptation to rush off into the bathroom after making love. Keep a towel or supply of tissues by the side of the bed if you really want to avoid damp patches on the sheets. Or take a shower or a bath together. Be careful not to say anything that could be regarded as critical. Men are more sensitive, more vulnerable than they may seem to be. If you want to talk, avoid household problems. Talking about the drains or the bathroom shelf he hasn't put up is hardly likely to keep him in a romantic mood. Talk about plans for the future, real hopes and ambitions and aspirations. Tell him how wonderful he is and how much he is loved.

Chapter 5

Extras

Games and Gadgets

In 1737 a man called George Baggerley who lived in Leicester, England was taken to court for having sewn together the *labia* of his wife Dorothy. His defence was that he was merely trying to make his wife more sexually attractive.

In ancient China it was common for a woman to insert a necklace of four balls into her partner's anus. She would pull out one ball at a time as they made love. The final ball would be pulled out as she reached orgasm, thus helping to ensure that he ejaculated at the same moment.

It was also common in ancient China for men to wear a tight ring around their penises. The rings were designed to help maintain a large erection.

Some members of African tribes have small bells attached to the front part of their penises. These are designed to provide extra friction and to stimulate their partners. In other tribes a small piece of bone is pierced horizontally through the glans of the penis to increase its width.

Through the centuries men and women have tried all sorts of things to stimulate their sexual appetite and improve their performance. This chapter is not comprehensive but it should give you an idea of some of the games and gadgets and habits and customs that have been, or still are, popular.

👫 Audiences

In Cambodia in the twelfth century it was customary for brides to lose their virginity not to their husbands but to a priest. Moreover they lost it in the presence of all their wedding guests. The priest was highly paid and allowed only to perform this remarkable service once a year. The rest of the time he was supposed to remain celibate.

Throughout history there are examples of sex being enjoyed in front of an audience. In eighteenth-century England wedding guests sometimes crowded into the bridal suite and watched while the groom deflowered his bride. Bridesmaids would lead the blushing bride into the bedroom, undress her and lay her down on the bed. The groom would then be brought in by his friends. Everyone would gather round and cheer and make practical suggestions.

Today there are some couples and some individuals who get a special thrill out of performing, either before a small group of friends or before a large audience of strangers. Those who prefer to observe rather than participate can attend live sex shows in many major cities around the world.

👫 Bondage

In old black and white movies the heroine invariably spent some of her time on screen tied up. Often she'd be stretched out on her back and tied to a railway line. She would eventually be rescued by the handsome hero who would pick her up in his arms and carry her off into the distance at the end of the film.

Bondage has come a long way since then. These days many couples add extra spice to their sex lives by tying one another up. Some women enjoy the feeling that they are being overpowered and forced to take part in sexual acts about which they would otherwise feel guilty. Being tied to the bed allows them to free themselves of guilt.

Not that it is only women who like being tied up; many men get a thrill from it too. And they don't usually have too much difficulty in finding female partners prepared to take the role of the aggressor.

Bondage enables men and women to submit to pleasurable experiences which they might otherwise find impossible to accept. And there seems little doubt that done properly it can increase the intensity of an orgasm and heighten sexual pleasure.

If you want to add bondage to your repertoire of sexual skills here are some practical hints and tips.

Remember that bondage is not about hurting – it's simply a trick to heighten your sexual pleasure. Feminine resistance may give a man a feeling of conquest and power. Feeling vulnerable and showing resistance can make a woman feel virginal and innocent. It can free her from all inhibitions. Reversing the roles produces a different range of emotional responses.

Start by stripping her either naked or down to flimsy underwear that is unlikely to get in the way later on. Remember that once she's tied up you won't be able to remove panties without ripping them. (Many women like having their clothes torn off. If you're planning this try to make sure that she isn't wearing her latest, most expensive silk underwear). Tie her to a bed (a four-poster is ideal but anything with legs will do) or a chair or even an upright post of some kind. Use pieces of cloth, old stockings, luggage straps or stretches of clothes-line to fasten her ankles and wrists so that she cannot move. Be firm but don't tie too tightly. And make sure you tie knots that can be undone afterwards. If you want to gag her (and she doesn't mind) use something soft and comfortable and make sure that it can be removed quickly and easily if necessary. Don't put a soft gag into her mouth, don't tie anything round her neck, don't tie her face down, don't try any of this after drinking and don't allow anyone you don't know and trust to do any of these things to you.

Once she's firmly tied just touch her skin gently with your fingers. Run your nails lightly down her arm and then down her thighs. Use all the areas of her skin that you know are sensitive. Gradually work your way around and towards her breasts. Kiss her skin softly with your lips. Try licking her nipples and blowing gently on them. After a minute or two of this she will be aroused. Prolong the agony as long as you can and then begin to masturbate her.

Move away from her occasionally if you like. Tease her a little.

Undress and ask her what she wants. Soon you will both realize that there is very little difference between agony and ecstasy. You will find it easy to push her to a point where she desperately wants relief from sexual frustration. Tell her what you are going to do to her. Do it as slowly as you can.

In the paragraphs above I've described him as the active participant and her as the passive partner. The roles can easily be reversed.

She can build him up almost to the point of ejaculation. And then stop and pull away from him. If she undresses slowly and provocatively he will soon be begging her not to stop. If she drags her fingernails slowly around his scrotum and touches his penis lightly with her fingertips he will probably develop an erection far larger than anything he has ever produced before.

Bondage should never be painful or dangerous. It should always be something both partners enjoy.

One final piece of advice: always arrange a code so that if for some reason the partner who is tied wants to be released the active partner will know that the request is serious.

🚹🚺 Chastity belts

The original chasity belts were made of metal, were heavy, cold and distinctly uncomfortable. They were intended to prevent rape and, contrary to popular belief, the key was usually hidden by the woman wearing the belt. The chastity belt was worn not because her husband doubted her virtue but because he doubted the ability of his friends to resist temptation in his absence.

Some modern lovers find the concept appealing even though they are not attracted by the reality of a metal contraption.

A fun alternative is for her to wear a pair of tight panties or a G-string and for him to try and make love to her without removing them. Some lovers find this variation more exciting than ordinary straight sex, perhaps just as an occasional alternative. It is often possible for both partners to reach an orgasm without penetration taking place. Stockings and suspenders tend to improve his chances of success. Tights diminish the chances of both participants.

Unmarried girls sometimes wear panties while making love

on the grounds that this will enable them to remain virgins. The point is debatable. It is, however, important to remember that it is possible for her to become pregnant unless he ejaculates well clear of her vagina. Panties are unlikely to prove an effective contraceptive.

 Exhibitionism

Both men and women may get pleasure from exhibiting their bodies in public. Topless and nudist beaches are now commonplace along the world's coastlines.

Away from the beach exhibitionism is usually regarded as a male phenonemon. Men often wear tight trousers – just a zip's pull away from arrest – but the dirty old man in a dirty old raincoat who exposes himself in public places to unsuspecting girls and maiden ladies is a relatively rare beast. Such men deserve punishment for the offence they cause but are invariably shy, vulnerable and lacking in self-confidence. They expose themselves in order to get female respect for their masculinity and can usually be deflated by a few derogatory remarks. Only rarely do 'flashers' become anything more than an offensive nuisance and embarrassment, although they frequently frighten their victims.

Surprisingly, perhaps, it is today's women who are most likely to want to expose their bodies in public. In France and Italy women frequently remove their clothes on television in the hope of winning modest prizes. In every country in the world women wear clothes which are clearly designed to accentuate and/or expose. The popular emphasis is on provocation.

Thousands of women (far more women than men) happily pose for nude photographs (often taken with instant cameras) and many then allow their partners to show the results to their friends. A growing number of 'soft porn' men's magazines regularly publish photographs taken by boyfriends and husbands. Clearly many women are excited by the knowledge that photos of their nude bodies will be made available to large numbers of complete strangers.

Fetishes

The word 'fetish' is overused. A man who gets a bit of a thrill when his partner wears black stockings and suspenders is not a fetishist. A woman who gets a kick out of wearing patent-leather high-heeled shoes and parading naked in front of her lover is not a fetishist. A man who likes his partner to dress up in provocative clothes or a uniform occasionally is not a fetishist. A woman who enjoys making love on satin sheets is not a fetishist.

A fetish is only a fetish when it takes over. The liking gradually becomes obligatory, swamping every other sensation. Eventually the fetishist is unable to obtain sexual satisfaction without the shoes or the panties or the stockings or the jewellery or the gloves. The need to touch and fondle the desired item becomes the only thing that produces arousal. Indeed, he or she may be able to reach orgasm with the item alone. The object eventually distances him or her from sexual intercourse and takes over his or her life.

Pornography

As long as there have been artists there has been pornography. Centuries before cameras were invented artists were busy creating sexually explicit statues and drawings. In ancient India, sex was thought of as an expression of the divine spirit and explicit erotic carvings were proudly displayed alongside religious objects in temples. In ancient China and Japan, painted scrolls which contained detailed drawings of sexual positions were widely available as the first pillow books. Some of the drawings and carvings were designed to entertain, amuse and arouse, others as educational tools.

This freedom of expression which has always been far less apparent in the West disappeared for a long time and up until fairly recently sexually explicit books, magazines, photographs and films were regarded as obscene or 'dirty'. Because the possession of such items was illegal, most of the sex industry went underground and became dominated by criminals.

Today censorship has been relaxed for those publishing what is called 'soft' pornography – material which is not usually explicit and which is unlikely to offend the majority of potential customers. There are certain basic, bizarre ground rules. So, for example, publishers are allowed to produce and freely distribute photographs of women simulating sexual orgasm or close-up photographs of women's genitalia but they are not allowed to publish photographs of men with erect penises.

It is widely believed that all modern pornography is aimed specifically at men and that women are uninterested in, and unlikely to be aroused by, any sexually explicit material.

This isn't true. The fact is that in the first three quarters of this century – when the sex industry was developing – women were reluctant to admit that they found pornography stimulating. Having been brought up to regard such material as offensive they vigorously denied that they ever found themselves being aroused by watching erotic films or reading erotic books.

However, more recent surveys have shown, without any doubt, that women are often as easily stimulated as men by the right sort of material. It seems that women tend to prefer material in which sex is mixed with romance but the explosion in the demand for steamy 'bodice-ripper' novels, in which the heroine does far more than dream of her lover's skills in bed, proves that women's appetite for sexually stimulating material has risen and is still rising.

Some women even enjoy looking at photographs of naked women in newspapers and magazines. And they like tapes, photographs and stories in which women are shown seducing men and taking an active, controlling part in sex.

In a recent German survey, over 500 male and female students were shown a wide variety of pornographic material. A few of the women were irritated, shocked or disgusted but on the whole there was little difference in the way the two sexes responded.

Four out of five women said that reading or watching sexually explicit material produced some genital sensation, a quarter said that they felt vaginal lubrication and one in ten said that they felt their breasts begin to tingle. Two of the women had orgasms while reading or watching pornography.

The male reactions were similar. Slightly more than four out of every five had an erection, a quarter reported that there had been some slight leekage of seminal fluid and eight ejaculated.

Afterwards both the men and the women reported that there had been a rise in their sexual desire and that the material had affected their sexual behaviour. More women were stimulated to have sex by the material than men.

In another survey, men and women were shown a film of a rape scene. Both the men and the women were highly aroused by the scene but admitted afterwards that they were confused by their reactions. Many of the men said that they felt dismayed that they had been stimulated by the rape. They felt guilty and anxious and could not understand what had happened. Some of the women who were aroused were also frightened – both by what they saw on the screen and by their own reactions. However unpleasant the reality may be there is no denying the fact that many men and women do find the thought of rape sexually stimulating. It is this phenomenon which explains why so many women and men are sexually aroused by bondage games (see page 101).

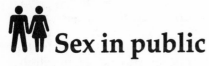 # Sex in public

Many people have sex out of doors. Making love in a country field, on a sandy beach (with a rug to prevent the sand becoming an unbearable nuisance) or in the sea (with one foot on the bottom) can all be exciting.

For some the sense of excitement is enhanced if there is a real risk of discovery.

Making love in a public place is for many a regular habit. Surprisingly large numbers of men and women have made love in parks, on trains, in aeroplanes, on boats and in lifts. The hazard of discovery can undoubtedly add a thrill to a sexual relationship that has become stale and uninspired.

If you don't want to go all the way – and risk discovery, embarrassment and possible arrest – then there are things you can try to liven up dull journeys or dinner parties. For example, while sitting opposite one another in a restaurant try slipping off your shoes and, under cover of the table and table cloth, using your toes as fingers to stimulate each other. He can use the pad of his big toe to stimulate her clitoris or vulva. She can use her toes to masturbate him as close to an orgasm as seems appropriate.

🕴️ Sharing

A remarkable number of men, whether married or not, readily confess that in their most regular and most erotic fantasy they allow, or rather encourage, their usual partners to make love to one or more men. The arranged infidelity usually takes place in the husband's presence so that he can watch and make love to his wife after the other man has finished with her. Sometimes the wife will be encouraged to accommodate the two men at the same time, offering one man her vagina and the other her mouth.

Sharing a woman is a well-established male ritual which some experts argue helps to eradicate potentially dangerous male aggression. It is certainly not uncommon for several men to choose to enjoy the favours of one prostitute in preference to the favours of several. A few psychologists argue that men who have this fantasy are hiding homosexual tendencies and that they really want to have sex with the other man. There seems little evidence to support this theory. Other experts claim that this dream is common to masochists, men who obtain satisfaction from taking a step down the hierarchical ladder. There may be a much simpler explanation. It may be that some men suspect that they have difficulty in satisfying their partner and decide that sharing her with other men would provide a stimulating solution. Male friendship bonds are often difficult to analyse.

It's impossible to be accurate about how often this fantasy turns into reality, but it's certainly not a rare phenomenon. Sometimes the third (and fourth, and more) member of the group will be a complete stranger picked up in a pub or contacted through a magazine. Often the dream becomes reality while on holiday. Commonly, however, the additional male is a close relative or friend of the husband. The man may be staying the night for some reason.

Why do so many women agree to what some might see as a humiliating experience?

It isn't just alcohol that breaks down the barriers, though that undoubtedly helps. Sometimes a woman who normally has difficulty in reaching a climax will find the prospect irresistible. Sometimes a woman whose married sex life has become dull and predictable will welcome the opportunity to add a little extra excitement.

There are of course real dangers with sharing. First, there is the risk of infection. And second there is the risk that the introduction of an additional partner will result in permanent damage being done to a long-standing relationship. Guilt, anger, confusion and depression are all common consequences.

🏃🏼 Skin piercing

Piercing the skin so that pieces of jewellery can be worn is a well-established human custom. Over the years millions of men and women have decorated themselves in this way.

In ancient Egypt, for example, both men and women wore ear-rings. In England, Charles I had a pearl stud in one ear. Today ear-rings are almost as common among men as among women.

Nipple piercing has been popular for centuries too in some countries. In France, in the reign of Louis XIV, the Church condoned the wearing of low-necked dresses as long as the women wearing them had gold rings piercing their exposed nipples. The Church reasoned that the gold rings meant that the breasts were not entirely naked. Today, nipple piercing is an increasingly common fashion in many parts of the world and is considered sexually alluring by many women and men.

Nor is it uncommon now for women and men to have their sexual organs pierced and fitted with jewellery.

Women sometimes have rings pushed through their *labia*. The idea is that the weight of the rings will pull down the clitoral hood and stimulate the clitoris. Women also claim that while wearing labial rings their partners are better able to bring them to orgasm. Some men say that they find labial jewellery visually stimulating.

It is now not uncommon for a man to have a ring through his foreskin, *frenulum*, glans or scrotum. Apart from decoration the aim is to be able to offer his partner greater stimulation.

Piercing can be dangerous if done carelessly. Important structures may be damaged and infection is a major risk. Some doctors now agree to provide a piercing service to prevent their patients patronizing back-street clinics.

Vibrators and other sex aids

The artifical phallas or dildo has for centuries been a common piece of sexual equipment. Sculptured figures from ancient Babylonia and India show women with dildos in their hands. Greek women living 2000 years ago used sophisticated dildos made of leather and fitted with mechanical devices which enabled them to become erect.

Modern vibrators are powered by small batteries. Often made in the shape of a penis, they can hasten the development of an orgasm. They're mostly used by women, who can get great pleasure from placing them on or around the clitoris. But men can enjoy them too, either applied to the penis or around or inside the anus.

If one half of a partnership uses a vibrator alone, it can eventually divide the partnership in two; orgasms are so easy to obtain with vibrators that human partners can become redundant. But when used as a sexual aid by two people, either for simulated intercourse or even as a masturbatory aid, vibrators can bring a spark into a love affair. A woman who has difficulty in reaching an orgasm when having straight sex may find that a vibrator provides her with a welcome release from frustration. If her partner has suffered from feelings of inadequacy he will probably welcome the vibrator's arrival. It should always be remembered that the vibrator is an aid to good sex not a rival or a threat. A vibrator can't cuddle or kiss or caress.

It is also important to remember that vibrators can be dangerous if used carelessly. One man put a vibrator into his anus and an hour or two later arrived at hospital casualty department complaining of a vibrating umbilicus. The vibrator had worked its way up his intestinal tract. The surgeons had to wait until the battery ran down before operating to remove it.

Other sex aids can prove hazardous too. One issue of the *British Medical Journal* contained three reports of men who had been compromised by vacuum cleaners. The first man, a sixty-year-old, said that he had been changing the plug on the vacuum cleaner while he was waiting for his wife to come back from a shopping expedition. For some reason he had chosen to do this electrical repair work in the nude. The vacuum cleaner miraculously turned itself on and pulled his penis into the pipe. The penis suffered nasty tears and lacerations.

In the second case, a sixty-five-year-old railway signalman bent down to pick up his tools and caught his penis in the suction pipe of a vacuum cleaner that had been accidently left switched on.

And in the final case, a forty-nine-year-old man was vacuuming a friend's staircase in a loose-fitting dressing-gown when, as he moved to pull the plug out of the socket, his dressing-gown blew open. His penis, too, was sucked directly into the vacuum-cleaner pipe where it remained jammed until the hospital staff could free him.

Not that men are the only sex vulnerable to accidents of this type. Every year thousands of women visit their family doctors and local casualty departments with items mysteriously stuck in their vaginas. Candles and other similarly shaped objects are commonplace but I know of doctors who have retrieved far more bizzare bits and pieces. One doctor pulled out a short gear stick complete with knob. Another rescued a small bust of Napolean. And a third had to 'deliver' a set of false teeth. Cucumbers, courgettes and bananas are popular discoveries in this area.

It is, of course, possible to purchase peculiarly shaped condoms, designed for 'extra stimulation'. I have never, however, met any woman who has derived extra pleasure from these devices and they may be structurally unsound so should not be used as contraceptives.

The message should be clear. Take care with any sex aid. Few will be fatal unless you are likely to die of embarrassment!

Sexual Fantasies

Until fairly recently it was assumed that only men had sexual fantasies. It is now known not only that women also have sexual fantasies but that they fantasize more often during sex than men.

Sexual fantasies begin in early adolescence. Girls start, on average, two years earlier than boys, with idealized fantasies. They usually imagine a lover who will take charge of them and their lives, who will whisk them off and protect them. They have emotional fantasies rather than sexual ones. They fantasize about being loved.

When adolescent boys start fantasizing their dreams are largely physical. They often fantasize about seducing beautiful women whom they know – often mothers of their friends or friends of their mother. They fantasize about sex more than about romance.

In adulthood more women than men fantasize during sex. Women who frequently enjoy positive vivid daydreams are likely to have remarkably rich fantasies during sex. Their fantasies may help them feel aroused and may help take them to orgasm. Fantasies help members of both sexes to overcome inhibitions.

Some men and women enrich and enhance their sexual fantasies by looking at sexually explicit magazines, by watching slightly blue movies or by reading books which contain steamy sex scenes. Most ordinary men and women are stimulated by well-written, well-produced pornography in which sex is mixed with romance and adventure, rather than by crude, explicit pornography.

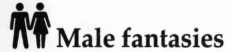 **Male fantasies**

A third of all men have fantasies while making love. Many men have sexual fantasies when they are not making love. The fantasies men have are similar to the ones women have, but there are differences. Here are some of the most popular sexual fantasies, not in any particular order:

1.   Replacing their usual sexual partner with another woman,

occasionally a film star or celebrity but more commonly a woman they know or a past lover. Neighbours, friends and virgins are popular
2. Having sex with a woman who resists but finds it so exciting that she eventually gives in
3. Watching other people have sex
4. Watching another man or several other men have sex with their wife or girlfriend
5. Having group sex
6. Having a homosexual encounter
7. Being sexually abused by women. One man reported that his favourite sexual fantasy was to be tied to a conveyor belt and carried past a line of beautiful women. Each time the belt came to a new women she would climb on top of him and make love to him. When she'd finished the conveyor belt would take him on to the next woman
8. Having sex in public while an audience watches
9. Making love in bizarre surroundings, perhaps somewhere very 'proper' such as a court room
10. Taking part in a threesome with a man and a woman

12. Taking part in a threesome with two women
13. Watching two women have sex together. One of the two women may be a wife or girlfriend, the other may be a friend, relative (for example, a sister-in-law) or neighbour
14. Watching a regular partner dressed in sexy clothes, possibly in a public place, maybe working as a prostitute
15. Being raped by a woman
16. Being spanked
17. Being involved in food fights with women
18. Being sexually abused by a nurse while in hospital
19. Being urinated on by a woman
20. Forcing a woman to have oral sex against her will
21. Being a slave to a woman
22. Being subjected to anal sex by a woman equipped with a large dildo
23. Having sex with a woman with huge breasts
24. Dressing up in women's clothing – and being caught, exposed and humiliated
25. Spanking a woman
26. Forcing a woman to have sex with an animal.

Female fantasies

Women's fantasies are, like men's, often incredibly complex and sophisticated. They are also often very indecent. It used to be thought that when women fantasized they dreamed of being carried off by handsome Arab sheiks on horseback, or of romantic affairs with fim stars. Not true. Women's fantasies are as sexually explicit as men's.

Incidentally, there is evidence that women who have fantasies while they are masturbating are more likely to have orgasms than women who don't. Similarly, some women find it easier to reach orgasm during intercourse if they have fantasies.

Here are some of the most popular female sexual fantasies, in no particular order:

1. Being raped
2. Being forced to have sex in public
3. Being exposed or humiliated in public
4. Having sex with a loved partner in a public place

5. Having sex in extraordinary circumstances, for example at a meeting, with everyone applauding
6. Being forced to make love to young boys
7. Being forced to make love to an animal (dogs and horses are most popular) and/or being licked to orgasm by an animal
8. Being sexually abused by several men at once
9. Being taken by a stranger from behind, never seeing the man's face
10. Replacing their usual sexual partner with another man
11. Watching others have sex
12. Having idyllic sexual encounters with complete strangers who leave immediately after sex
13. Having lesbian encounters, with friends or strangers
14. Stripping on stage and getting lots of applause
15. Taking part in a group sexual encounter
16. Working as a prostitute and having to satisfy a large number of clients
17. Humiliating a man alone or with other women
18. Being forced to have oral sex with a man
19. Being tied down and used by one or more men
20. Being spanked
21. Having a male slave
22. Taking part in a threesome, with one of the men being a husband, lover or regular partner and the other being a stranger
23. Taking part in a threesome with one male and one female partner
24. Dressing in provocative clothing and teasing men at a party.

Do fantasies ever turn into reality

Sometimes, but not all that often. A fantasy is not necessarily a repressed wish. For example, women commonly fantasize about being taken forcibly or raped by several men at once and committed homosexuals often have vivid heterosexual fantasies. For them the fantasy is something quite different to the reality. Similarly men who fantasize about raping women should not feel guilty; the fantasy is a long way from the real thing.

Aphrodisiacs

A tremendous amount of nonsense has been written about aphrodisiacs in recent years. Many myths and legends have been built up around substances which have absolutely no useful effect, and some of which can kill you.

Rhinoceros horn acquired a reputation as an aphrodisiac because of its phallic shape. But the available evidence shows that it has absolutely no value to those who want to improve their sexual attractiveness or performance. Spanish fly, derived from the cantharis beetle which is found in southern Europe is another well-known aphrodisiac. The beetles are anaesthetized, dried and then heated until they disintegrate into powder. When taken, the powder causes a dilation of the blood vessels in the penis and can irritate and inflame the intestinal tract. There is no denying the fact that Spanish fly does have some sexual effect – it can even produce menstrual bleeding in women and can produce a long-lasting erection in men. But there's a heavy price to pay: Spanish fly can cause internal bleeding and can kill. Ginseng is widely regarded as an aphrodisiac because of the shape of its root. But like the horn of the rhinoceros the available evidence does not back up this theory. Yohimbine, from the yohimbe tree, does increase the flow of blood to the sexual organs and also increases nervous activity in that area. But people who have tried it say that the effect is purely genital and there is no accompanying sense of pleasure or satisfaction.

Vitamin E is widely promoted as a sexual aid. Throughout the world many companies have made large amounts of money by persuading men and women that taking vitamin E capsules will increase their sexual potency. But vitamin E earned its massive reputation as an aphrodisiac solely on the basis of a limited amount of research work done on rat fertility patterns. There is absolutely no evidence to support the contention that you'll be able to improve your sexual prowess by taking vitamin E.

Some experts claim that marijuana can increase sexual desire and pleasure but the only really useful effect it has is to remove any existing inhibitions. The available evidence suggests that marijuana may actually *lower* the amount of circulating testosterone (which is one of the most important sex hormones). Others have recommended amyl nitrate, claiming that if you break an ampoule of the stuff, saturate a piece of cotton wool and then inhale you will feel a great rush of sexual excitement. There is little doubt that amyl nitrate increases the blood supply to various parts of the body and can make an individual feel more excited, but there are real dangers with this product and it's certainly not safe for use as a general aphrodisiac. Many authorities claim that the drug helps to relax the anal sphincter and is, therefore, useful if two partners want to try anal intercourse. I think the hazards associated with its use far outweigh this slight practical value.

Psilocybe and amanita, obtained from two allegedly sexually potent magic mushrooms, are sometimes used separately and sometimes together. Amanita is said to give those who use it great energy and staying power. Some experimenters have reported that it produces forceful and unnaturally prolonged orgasms with repeated ejaculations and violent vaginal contractions. It also distorts the processes of thought and can produce terrifying results. Psilocybe has far less dramatic sexual effects but has a chemical structure quite similar to that of LSD; it is, in other words, a hallucinogenic drug. I certainly do not recommend either of these substances as aphrodisiacs.

The Mexican desert just south of the Rio Grande is not the most hospitable spot in the world, but it is the home of a small rather ordinary-looking grey-green cactus known as *lophophora williamsii*. This plant, which rarely grows more than 3 inches (7.5cms) high is the source of one of the world's most powerful drugs – mescaline. The local Indians once used the cactus in their most sacred ceremonies, treating it with enormous respect and regarding it primarily as a very powerful aphrodisiac. The warriors who collected the drug would abstain from all sexual contact for at least six weeks before setting off into the desert. Once they had found a plant, they would slice the top off, scoop out the tiny grooved button which contains the most concentrated form of mescaline, and rush back home. There virgins would chew the buttons of mescaline, then soak them in water in order to prepare a powerful ceremonial drink which would be used in sexual initiation rites. During these rites the village braves would systematically deflower all the virgins.

When the Spanish arrived in Mexico the representatives of the Catholic Church tried unsuccessfully to persuade the Indians to take the sacramental wafer instead of the mescaline button and to forgo the initiation rites in favour of hymn singing and prayers. They didn't have much success.

On the surface mescaline may sound very attractive. But there are two problems with it. First it has powerful hallucinogenic qualities. People who use it often have 'trips' which can vary from 'pleasant' to 'terrifying'. Second, it is an extremely addictive drug.

There are dozens of other herbs and chemicals which have at one time or another been recommended as aphrodisiacs. But having studied numerous scientific papers I'm afraid I have to tell you that I still haven't found any substance which is both effective and safe. There are chemicals which have a sexually stimulating effect – but they may kill you or permanently damage your health. And there are many safe products around which will do you no harm – but which will have no effect on your sexual desires or performance.

The truth is that the only real aphrodisiac is to be with someone you love and care about. That *is* a turn-on. Nevertheless, there are a number of things you can do to improve your sex life, to turn yourself and your partner on. None of the following suggestions will revolutionize your sex life but some may help it.

 Alcohol

I have to include alcohol somewhere in this chapter, partly because it is widely used and partly because it does have some value as an aphrodisiac. I was tempted to list it at the beginning of this chapter among the useless and potentially hazardous products. However, I relented because, if taken in small quantities, alcohol *can* be useful as an aphrodisiac – releasing inhibitions and suppressing fears and anxieties.

Alcohol works as an aphrodisiac in two ways. It depresses the restrictive control centres in the brain and thereby allows desires which are normally suppressed to surface. In addition it causes a general dilatation of the body's superficial blood vessels and produces a generalized skin glow.

The snag is that although a small amount of alcohol will depress the inhibitory parts of your brain, and allow you to do things that you would otherwise want to think twice about, a larger amount of alcohol will depress the rest of your brain. It will make you feel sad, it will remove the inhibitions that normally stop you showing inappropriate emotions such as anger, it may change your personality completely. And, most important of all for a supposed aphrodisiac, it will have a damaging effect on your ability to have sex. Too much alcohol will make a man impotent and a woman dry, frigid and quite uninterested in sex.

It should be clear from all this that if you want to use alcohol as an aphrodisiac it's vitally important to get the amount you use absolutely right. I would suggest that for most people one and a half to two glasses of wine will be enough. Some people, particularly those with larger bodies, may be able to drink three glasses before their sexual skills start to disappear.

Alcohol usually begins to produce a result about fifteen minutes after it has been drunk. If food is consumed at the same time, the rate at which the alcohol is absorbed into the blood-stream slows down. Soda water increases this rate but reduces the length of time that its potency lasts.

What should you drink? Beer isn't really suitable. The heavy fluid intake inevitably leads to bladder distention. But wines or spirits are fine. Champagne is excellent because of its romantic associations. Some experts say that green Chartreuse is very good.

 **Chocolate**

Montezuma, the Aztec king, collected wives and concubines the way other men collect hotel towels. By the time he'd really settled down he'd acquired a harem of 700 beautiful women. Keeping that number of women sexually satisfied would pose a problem to most men but Montezuma obtained the necessary stamina and sexual strength by drinking huge quantities of a special brew. His palace aphrodisiac even gave him the strength to deal with a few affairs on the side – proving that even if you've got 700 wives the grass can always be greener in someone else's bedroom.

The basic ingredient of the king's brew was chocolate, something traditionally used by Aztecs in ceremonies honouring Xochiquetzal, their unique and generous goddess of love.

Chocolate was introduced into Spain in the early seventeenth century. Its use spread throughout Europe and thousands in

Spain, France and Italy valued it as an aphrodisiac. But by the nineteenth century the value of chocolate as a sexual stimulant had been questioned and it was more often given as a love token than used as a sexual aid.

Then, a year or two ago, researchers in New York discovered that chocolate contains a chemical called phenylethylamine – a substance related to the amphetamines. It seems that Montezuma knew what he was doing: chocolate can stimulate the emotions and may therefore have a slight effect as an aphrodisiac. Phenylethylamine is the 'love chemical' which helps us fall in love.

But a word of warning: chocolate is rich in calories and too much of it will make you fat. Although there are exceptions, that isn't usually sexy.

Incidentally, cooking chocolate is usually more potent than ordinary eating chocolate.

 # Clothes

Clothes can be a terrific turn-on.

It is usually women who dress to charm or seduce. By carefully selecting what she chooses to wear a woman can reveal much about her mood and attitude towards sex. Black stockings, high-heeled shoes, uplift bras, garter belts, skin-tight leather trousers or jeans, low-cut dresses, skin-tight sweaters, flimsy see-through nighties, diaphanous blouses worn with no bra underneath – there are dozens of items in the average women's wardrobe which are designed more for sex appeal than for protection against the cold.

It's also important to remember that although a woman may be dressed in extremely prim and proper top clothes (a formal black dress for example) she can still wear erotic and stimulating clothes underneath it. Many men are excited by the knowledge that their partner is wearing very flimsy underwear.

Although it is usually women who dress to please it isn't *only* women who use clothes to enhance their sex appeal. Many men take great care with their choice of clothes.

Whatever sex you are you will be far better able to dress to seduce if you know what turns your partner, or prospective partner, on.

👫 Dieting

If you're overweight, flabby and out of condition you'll be in poor shape for sex – and your sexual confidence will probably be low too. You'll be reluctant to undress in front of your partner, unable to get into some sexual positions, embarrassed about the fact that your weight may make your partner feel uncomfortable, and low on stamina. If you have folds of stomach fat hanging over your sexual organs you may find it difficult to get aroused and difficult to reach an orgasm.

Losing weight will boost your sex life in a number of ways. But I should, perhaps, point out that skinny isn't too sexy either. Most men prefer their partners to be curvaceous rather than 'model thin' and most women prefer men to have some meat on their ribs. Check a weight/height table and find out the average sort of weight for your height. By and large you should aim at keeping within half a stone of your ideal weight.

👫 Exercise

In America a study of 8,500 women showed that regular exercise makes it easier for women to become sexually aroused and makes them better lovers! According to the survey 40 per cent of women who exercise regularly say that they get turned on more easily than they did before they started exercising. One quarter of the women interviewed say that regular exercise increases their desire for sex and a third say that since taking up exercise they've made love far more often. Nine out of ten women say that exercise gives them more confidence in bed.

It isn't difficult to explain this apparently remarkable finding. Women who exercise regularly and whose bodies are firm and slender are less likely to feel shy or embarrassed about being seen naked or about making love. In addition the fitter and healthier you are the greater will be your capacity for exercise, your enthusiasm, your ability to get into new positions and your stamina.

A study involving men at the University of California produced similar results, showing that men who do most exercise have most sex. For nine months a sample of 115 men did ninety minutes of strenuous exercise for five days every week. They made love three times a week. A similar sized sample of men did far less exercise, and made love an average of just twice a week.

Regular exercise that you enjoy is one of the best aphrodisiacs there is. But don't do too much! If you come home from the gym exhausted and hardly able to move your love life won't get much of a boost.

 Food

An awful lot of nonsense has been written about foods. I've seen it said that if you want to look sexy, be sexy and act sexy you must take great care to boost your intake of certain minerals. I've seen women encouraged to take magnesium to improve their breasts. I've seen men advised to take zinc because it will boost the size of their penis, increase the amount of sperm they produce and enhance their sexual performance. I've seen lecithin recommended to men who want to increase the quality and quantity of their sperm. I know of people who suggest that vitamin B will prevent impotence. I've read articles suggesting that nucleic acid, iron, potassium and phosphorus all act as aphrodisiacs and are all vital for a good sex life. I've already dealt with vitamin E in my introduction to this chapter.

To a certain extent all this is true. If your body is *short* of any essential vitamins, minerals or other constituents then your sex life, and the rest of your life, will undoubtedly suffer. An absence of a specific mineral or vitamin from your diet will affect your ability to have and enjoy a good sex life. A constant diet of junk food will reduce your energy levels. But if you eat a normal, healthy, balanced diet taking extra vitamins or minerals will have no specific effect on your sex life. You'll be wasting your money.

Apart from vitamins and minerals there are dozens of different types of food that are recommended for their aphrodisiacal qualities. Many of them have won their reputation because of their shape rather than their constituents. Figs have a 'sexy' reputation because some people think they look like the vulva of a woman. Cucumbers, bananas, carrots and other similarly shaped foods have a reputation for being sexy because of their resemblance to the phallus. The avocado pear has a reputation as an aphrodisiac because it is the same sort of shape as a woman's womb. The Aztecs had such a high regard for the aphrodisiac qualities of the avocado that they kept all their virgins indoors during the avocado season.

Some foods have a sexy reputation because of their smell. So, foods with a 'musky' odour such as asparagus, artichokes, truffles and mushrooms are regarded as aphrodisiacs.

Other foods have acquired their reputation over the centuries. Steak is regarded as good for love-making because in the thirteenth century the Tartars used to ride for days when making raids on distant tribes. They frequently arrived too exhausted for any pillaging let alone any raping. To give themselves the energy they needed, they learned to pack spiced raw beef underneath their saddles so that, when a suitable moment presented itself, they could leap off their horses, eat the steak and get the energy for a little impromptu love-making. Steak tartare is still considered to be the most stimulating meat dish. Louis XIV's mistress spiced up the old king's love life with asparagus hollandaise prepared from eggs and asparagus; she reckoned both had powerful aphrodisiacal qualities. Caviare got its reputation through Rasputin; he claimed it to be his favoured aphrodisiac.

The long-established association between oysters and sex is difficult to explain, although oysters do contain chemicals related to human sex hormones and are rich in iodine which helps to keep the thyroid going. Some observers claim that the opening oyster shell reminds them of a woman. Whatever the reason for its popularity, the association seems appropriate since oysters have extraordinary complex sex lives. Some are born sexless and only decide later what sex they are going to be. Others change sex when they are fully grown. And some change backwards and forwards as the fancy takes them.

Honey probably has a reputation as an aphrodisiac for the simple but excellent reason that it is rich in energy. Clearly any energy-rich food is going to be useful to an energetic lover. Exercise can lead to a low blood sugar level which can in turn lead to a feeling of anxiety or even panic. Some enthusiatic and energetic lovers eat glucose sweets or dextrose tablets (the sort produced for sportsmen and climbers) before a hectic love-making session.

So, what sort of foods will enhance your sex life? And which foods are likely to damage it?

I'd recommend that you avoid very fatty or starchy foods, and avoid caffeine-rich drinks (ground coffee contains more than instant coffee which contains more than tea or cola drinks) since caffeine is a stimulant which is likely to make you edgy and nervous. Avoid heavy meals (your mother was right: don't exercise on a full stomach) and if you're preparing a meal try to choose foods that you know he or she likes best. Light, spicy foods are often good. Try to include fresh vegetables and fresh fruit if you can.

👫 Oil of wintergreen

The active ingredient in oil of wintergreen is methyl salicylate which is closely related to aspirin. When applied to the skin it has a slightly irritating effect and is widely used as a liniment for the relief of rheumatism and other pains. However, this irritating effect can be stimulating if the oil is applied directly to the penis and scrotum and the vulva and surrounding region. The solution will increase the flow of blood to the genital area and may help during the arousal phase. But is vitually important only to use a very dilute solution, for example, one part oil of wintergreen to nine parts water.

Some authorities suggest that if one partner holds a little dilute oil of wintergreen in his or her mouth and then practises oral sex on the other the effect can be extremely successful. I must repeat that it's important to use a very dilute solution and vital not to swallow the mixture since it can be poisonous if taken internally. Whichever dilution you use this is not an aphrodisiac I recommend.

👫 Perfumes

For centuries perfumes have been used as aids in the process of seduction. It wasn't all that long ago that a bill was laid before the English Houses of Parliament suggesting that if any woman had used perfume to gain a proposal of marriage then the marriage should be annulled. In 1770 Pope Pius the Faithful once decreed that merchants handling musk should be excommunicated, blaming them for an excess of adultery and fornication.

Over the years it has become clear that the strongest effects can be obtained by using perfumes derived from the glandular secretions of other animals. Ambergris, a waxy grey material produced by sperm whales, has been revered for centuries. But musk is most widely recognized as a sexually stimulating perfume. Obtained from the anal glands of the musk deer, it has an intensely powerful aroma and may remain stimulating for twelve to fourteen hours after a single application. Sunshine or heat of any kind will enhance the smell. The workmen who constructed palaces for Arabian princes used to mix musk with the mortar so that when the sun shone and the bricks warmed up the air would become heavy with sexually arousing perfume.

Despite the power associated with musk and other perfumes, artificial smells aren't always necessary. Both men and women produce chemical substances called pheromones which are designed to arouse and stimulate members of the opposite sex, and these can be far more arousing than artificial perfumes derived from other sources. Several groups of researchers have shown that the smells associated with the secretions produced by the vaginas of non-ovulating women are far less attractive to men than the smells produced by secretions during ovulation. It seems clear, therefore, that the production of pheromones is designed to attract men to women at a time when the women are most likely to conceive. If a group of men gather round one woman at a party then it may be that she is ovulating.

Pheromones are powerful but I should perhaps point out that some other human smells (notably stale sweat) are distinctly unattractive. In order to obtain the best use of your natural pheromones you should bathe several hours before meeting someone you want to attract. This will remove any stale or unpleasant odours while leaving plenty of time for seductive pheromones to develop.

♟️ Prescribed drugs

There is no specific aphrodisiac available on prescription but over the years doctors have found several well-known prescribed drugs to have an aphrodisiac effect. For example, some reports show that a drug used in the treatment of high blood pressure and a drug used to treat Parkinson's disease can both increase sexual interest.

The most effective aphrodisiac is, however, an appetite suppressant used to help slimmers. One doctor writing in the medical journal *The Lancet* reported that a forty-year-old woman took the drug to help reduce her appetite. Her husband had a good job over a hundred miles away from home and used to commute at weekends; in the week he stayed in a room near to his office. But after his wife had been on the drug for a few weeks he had to get a lower-paid job nearer to home in order to be available to satisfy his wife's greatly increased sexual demands.

Chapter 6

 Problems and Difficulties

Loss of Interest

The most common sexual problem of all is a lack of interest, a reduction in sex drive, a fall off in the number of times a week, a month or a year. When men and women are asked to list the things that worry them about sex they put 'lack of interest' right at the top. It comes well ahead of problems such as impotence, premature ejaculation or orgasmic difficulties in women.

There are all sorts of reasons why people lose their interest in and enthusiasm for sex. In the following pages I will outline the most common.

 Exhaustion

In most hospitals where there is living accommodation for both doctors and nurses there are strict rules designed to protect the nurses from the doctors. Most of the time they don't need to bother. Doctors working over a hundred hours a week just don't have the energy for nurse seduction. The same problem affects thousands of men and women whose daily commitments are so great that they gradually lose interest in sex. Even if they could find the time they wouldn't be able to find the energy. It isn't just men and women with careers who suffer from exhaustion; the same problem is also common among housewives who have several young children to look after.

The only way to deal with this problem is to sort out your priorities and allocate time more carefully.

Boredom

One day many years ago, President Coolidge was visiting a farm in his native America with his wife. Soon after their arrival the two dignitaries were taken off on separate tours. When Mrs Coolidge passed the chicken pens she asked the keeper if the rooster copulated more than once a day.

'Dozens of times,' replied the keeper.

'Please tell that to the president,' said Mrs Coolidge with a sly smile.

When the president arrived at the chicken pens the keeper passed on the information, as requested.

'Same hen, every time?' asked President Coolidge.

'Oh no, Mr President,' answered the keeper. 'A different one each time.'

The president nodded wisely. 'Please tell that to Mrs Coolidge,' he instructed the keeper.

At the start of a new sexual relationship most couples can't get enough of one another. But as the weeks, months and years go by the urge tends to weaken. Familiarity breeds contentment. This easing off is not peculiar to the human species; it's something that happens to other mammals. For them, too, a new partner triggers an increase in sexual activity.

The only explanation for this gradual but certain reduction in sexual activity is boredom. What was once exciting becomes monotonous as the initial buzz wears off. At the start of a relationship most couples use different techniques to escape from repetition and to bring new sensations to their sex life. But the possibilities are limited and soon exhausted. Eventually a comfortable pattern develops, reactions become predictable and over the years a relationship that was based on sex becomes – with fortune – a relationship based on friendship in which sex plays just a part, alongside tenderness and companionship.

There is nothing wrong with this change. It is inevitable. But many people worry when they realize that they aren't having sex as often as they used to. They think that there must be something wrong with them. They suspect that their relationship must be fragile if they aren't still making love every day. They blame fatigue, overwork and other possible factors. They read surveys in popular magazines which claim (inaccurately) that everyone has sex every other day and they feel inadequate.

There is no one solution to this problem. Flowers, candle-lit dinners, romantic weekends, stockings and suspenders, and weekends away from it all can put some zest, some thrills and some sparkle back into a well-developed relationship. But nothing can help recapture that initial sense of physical excitement, that intense feeling of insatiability. Wise couples recognize that sexual habits and patterns do change – in quality, quantity and significance – with time. Sex may still be important but it is no longer the sole reason for living.

👫 Mood changes

Our sex drive is closely linked to our mood. A loss of interest in sex is often associated with a feeling of depression. There can be psychological causes (perhaps worry about money, work or children) or physical causes (for example, the sort of hormone changes that occur during or after childbirth or the menopause).

When there is a cause for a mood change the problem will not be solved until the basic cause has been dealt with. If you feel depressed or suspect that you could be suffering from any physical problem then you should visit your doctor and ask for advice and help.

 Intolerance

I've used the word 'intolerance' to cover all the things that can really go wrong with a relationship. If a couple grow apart and begin to dislike one another then there is little doubt that their sex life will suffer along with everything else. Sometimes one member of a partnership will simply fall out of love with the other, or will find a new partner. Sometimes there are physical reasons. He may become fat, bloated and bald, taking no care with his appearance, and as a result she may find him repulsive. She may become plump, 'comfortable' and dull; maybe she always wears sensible thermal underclothing. He may then feel that her sexual appeal has disappeared entirely. Sometimes there is mental intolerance. Minor troubles and disputes may accumulate. Eventually minor comments and habits will produce an angry response.

If you think that you and your partner could be growing apart in this way then your sex life will only recover if and when you can repair the damage to your relationship. You may need expert help to do this.

Drugs

I don't mean the sort of drugs that people buy illegally on street corners (although they can damage your sex life). I mean the much more common problem caused by prescribed drugs.

If your interest in sex has disappeared or your ability to enjoy sex has disappeared AND you are taking a prescribed drug then there is a very good chance that the drug you are taking is ruining your sex life.

Here are some of the drugs that most commonly cause problems. If you are taking any of the drugs on this list and you are having problems with your sex life then I strongly suggest that you talk to your doctor and ask if it is possible for you to be given an alternative. Don't suddenly stop tablets unless you've got your doctor's permission.

1. Propranolol (prescribed for anxiety, high blood pressure and heart disease)
2. Amitriptyline (prescribed for depression)
3. Clonidine (prescribed for menopausal problems, high blood pressure and migraine)
4. Imipramine (prescribed for depression)
5. Chlorpromazine (prescribed as a tranquillizer)
6. Thiazide diuretics (prescribed for high blood pressure and in the treatment of fluid retention)
7. Protriptyline (prescribed for depression)
8. Indoramin (prescribed for high blood pressure)
9. Labetolol (prescribed for high blood pressure)
10. Clomipramine (prescribed for depression)

Finally, don't forget that tranquillizers and sleeping tablets can cause a reduction in sexual interest and damage sexual performance.

 # Celibacy

It is not widely recognized but if you haven't made love for some time then your sex drive will shrink. After going without sex for a few months your natural sexual urges will gradually disappear. People who are celibate (either through choice or because they cannot find a suitable partner or because they are separated from their partner) often find that as time goes by their interest in sex drops.

There is a physical explanation for this phenomenon. If an adult human does not have sex regularly then the quantity of circulating sex hormones will fall over a period of months. Eventually the level will fall so low that sex becomes unimportant and potential opportunities may well be ignored, overlooked or rejected.

 Fear

The next major sex problem that affects apparently normal, healthy adults is fear. The following are some of the ways that fear can ruin your sex life.

Fear of discovery
If you have no home of your own, no place where you can make love in private, then your ability to enjoy sex may be severely hampered by your fear of discovery. It is difficult to have an orgasm if you are constantly waiting for the living-room door to fly open or for someone to tap on the car window and shine a torch in your face.

One young married couple who came to see me when I was working as a general practitioner were living with her parents. The house they shared had very thin walls. They were terrified that they would be heard. They only managed to consummate their marriage when they booked a weekend away in a comfortable hotel.

Fear of disease
AIDS is not a major threat to heterosexuals. But millions of men and women have been so terrified by what they've read in newspapers or seen on television that they are frightened to have sex – even with faithful, regular partners.

There is a comprehensive account of sexual transmitted diseases (including AIDS) on page 188.

Fear of pregnancy
Neither partner will be able to relax if pregnancy is a concern. The best solution is to seek help from a doctor. Alternatively, he can have a hair cut and buy a packet of 'anything else for the weekend, sir?'

You will find advice about contraception on page 177.

Fear of inadequacy
Thousands of men and women suffer agonies because they fear that their equipment is inadequate. My chapter starting on page 160 should provide reassurance.

Many perfectly capable and competent individuals are encouraged to worry by the way that sex is often described in magazines. Journalists who write glibly about 'the rights of women to enjoy multiple orgasms' are responsible for much dissatisfaction and unhappiness. There is pressure on both men and women to perform with a frequency and intensity that many find impossible. Women who fail to achieve orgasm are encouraged by writers in women's magazines to blame their partners for failing to prepare them properly or for failing to maintain their erections for long enough. I was once asked for help by a couple who claimed that they had a major problem. It turned out that he was unable to hold an erection for longer than forty-five minutes. His companion, who made love with one eye on the watch on her wrist, firmly believed that she had a right to expect at least an hour's love-making on each occasion. A man who cannot continue for as long as his partner wants may be told that he is suffering from premature ejaculation and advised to seek help. Can a man who can hold an erection for forty-five minutes really be described as a premature ejaculator? Unrealistic expectations produce anxiety and inadequacy.

Some so-called authorities on sexual matters claim that people who don't have sex several times a week and who don't try a wide range of variations need help. This is truly bizarre. One might as well argue that people who don't run marathons need help, or that people who have blonde hair need medical attention or that anyone who doesn't like playing chess needs advice.

Men and women are encouraged to believe that sex must be a transcendental experience. Reading popular novels and watching popular films encourages ordinary folk to believe that everyone else is capable of joys they have never begun to approach. She may expect him to spring at her like an angry lion. He may expect to wield a weapon two feet long, hard as steel. She may expect to experience orgasms which wrack her body and leave her sobbing, exhausted and drained. He may expect his semen to gush into her like lava.

If she misses an orgasm she may worry that there is something wrong with her hormones. He may worry that he is no longer attractive to her. The wit and romance, so important once, have been completely removed from sex. Their place have been taken by standards, rights and expectations. We may be more enlightened than those of our prudish ancestors who dressed their table legs in petticoats but we've created our own pressures and anxieties, our own range of social stresses.

It is men who have suffered most from this change. Women today are far more aware of their sexuality, far more willing to take part in sex, far more willing to take the lead. All that is good. But a few women, inspired by feminist dogma, have become unduly aggressive; they have acquired all the sins that they so despise in men.

This powerful minority hunt their orgasms with rare determination. To them the male organ is little more than a 'natural feel' vibrator. They refuse to accept any role that they consider demeaning or feminine. They refuse to dress up in stockings or suspenders, not because they are shocked by the thought but because they consider the suggestion politically unacceptable. This vociferous group of feminists have acquired far more media power than their numbers entitle them to. One such woman who consulted me complained that her partner could only ever manage between sixty and eighty 'in and out' strokes of his penis before he ejaculated. She told me that she regarded this as grossly unacceptable and demanded that I do something about it.

The problem for all of us is that we are too ready to accept the abnormal as the normal and far too shy to admit that we are not driven through life by the burning in our loins. The result is a great deal of unhappiness and dissatisfaction and disharmony and frustration. Guilts, self-doubts and inadequacies become mixed and produce a wide range of problems including, eventually, frigidity and impotence. All over the world there are millions of men and women who feel inadequate, who lack confidence and who are frightened of failure and the consequences of failure.

In the flurry of publicity that is given to the super sex claims of film stars and celebrities (notorious for their ability to exaggerate) we forget that you can have too much of a good thing, that quality is far more important than quantity and that sharing, understanding and enjoying one another are essential parts of a good, healthy and happy sex life.

Male Sexual Problems

Impotence and premature ejaculation are the two most common and best-known sexual problems to affect men. In the following pages I will also look at retarded ejaculation and priapism, which are far less common but nonetheless significant sexual problems.

 **Impotence**

Impotence always seems to be the end of the world to a previously virile male. It usually strikes at the most inopportune and embarrassing moments. Most – probably all – men are impotent at one time or another. The symptoms are simple: he cannot acquire an erection easily and/or if he gets one then it is either too feeble or too short-lived to enable him to penetrate his partner.

Here are some of the most likely causes:

1. Tiredness, often through overwork. It is quite normal to have difficulty in acquiring or maintaining an erection when tired
2. Prescribed drugs – particularly drugs which are used in the treatment of high blood pressure or depression
3. Fear. Many types of fear can produce impotence. A man will have difficulty in acquiring an erection if he is frightened of catching a disease, of being caught, of making his partner pregnant, of hurting her or causing himself pain
4. Inadequacy. Some men feel very inadequate about their bodies, not simply about the size or shape of their penises. Some men cannot comfortably make love to women whom they consider to be beautiful – they may feel happier with a woman who is very plain, who takes no pride in herself, or even a woman who is deformed. Blind prostitutes, prostitutes with amputated limbs and prostitutes with severe, disabling disorders often do surprisingly well
5. Anxiety about failure is a common cause of impotence. The risk of failure is proportional to the build-up. If a man really wants to impress his partner then the chances of his being

impotent are high. Men who worry about how well they are doing are also prone to impotence. A man who is making love to a woman he really loves for the first time will often discover that he is impotent; his desire to do well will be too much for him

6. Alcohol is a common cause of impotence. Alcohol increases the desire but too much will adversely affect performance (see page 118). Most 'leisure' drugs (from tobacco to heroin) can cause problems. Smoking is a major cause of impotence
7. Diseases such as diabetes can cause impotence
8. Guilt. A married man who tries to make love to another woman will be prone to impotence
9. Overweight. Men who are fat are more likely to suffer from impotence. (The woman on top positions are most suitable for men who are severely overweight – see page 67)
10. Memories can cause problems. A man who tries to make love in a room or bed he associates with someone else may suffer from impotence, as may a man who tries to make love to a woman who has been a friend or a former partner of a friend for many years.

Age does not really figure on the list of possible causes. Age can affect the amount of time a man must wait for his second erection but it is not itself a cause of impotence.

Now for some tips for the man suffering from impotence:

1. Remember that this problem affects probably every man in the world at one time or another. If you do occasionally get an erection (asleep or awake, alone or with a partner) then there is nothing wrong with your equipment. The problem is in your mind and can be conquered. The vast majority of cases of impotence fit into this category
2. The more you worry about the problem the worse it will get
3. If you are totally unable to have an erection at any time then your problem may need treatment with hormones. Talk to your doctor
4. Do not waste your money on any 'quack' remedy. Back in the eighteenth century in Italy, impotent men presented their sluggish and reluctant organs to St Damien and begged for help. Today men are more likely to pay for herbal products, monkey gland cures or other weird concoctions. Because of the shame and embarrassment that they feel, impotent men often visit 'quack' healers secretly – and dare not

complain when the product turns out to be worthless
5. Impotence can be considered a sign of intelligence. Men who have suffered serious damage to the front part of their brains are not able to worry; they have a constantly carefree expression and develop few wrinkles; they also have a great and consistent sexual desire which rarely falters.

If you are suffering from impotence you must slowly and gradually rebuild your confidence. You should try to deal with any anxieties or problems in other parts of your life and you should spend a little time learning how to relax. You will find it easier to conquer your impotence if you have a regular partner rather than a number of occasional partners or a succession of one-night stands. With new partners or one-night stands you will have to explain your problem to each new partner and will probably find it far more stressful.

Spend time on foreplay. Learn how to please your partner with your hands and mouth. If you know that you can bring your partner to orgasm before you have even entered her then the pressure on you will be reduced enormously. Try to relax with your partner as often as you can. Cuddle and kiss frequently. Maybe you can ask her to wear clothes which you find a turn-on. Don't be ashamed to allow your mind to escape into a fantasy world. Think of a situation which you find erotic and allow your mind to roam free and unfettered. It is quite true that you can't go to prison for what you're thinking. Allow your imagination to construct a powerfully erotic screenplay.

Some experts recommend that men who are suffering from impotence should make a decision to try not to have sex for six weeks. During that time, they say, you should concentrate on touching your partner. You should become adept at foreplay. Even if you get an erection you should not have sex. You should learn to relax and enjoy your partner. Bring her to orgasm with your hands and encourage her to do the same to you.

If, after six weeks, you are regularly getting erections then you can make love. If not, then you should extend your period of deliberate abstinence for another four weeks. Taking the pressure off in this way can work wonders.

Finally, if your erection is a poor one you will find that penetration is far easier to achieve if you lie side by side or if your partner sits on top of you. The missionary position is not good for men who suffer from partial impotence.

Premature ejaculation

Premature ejaculation has been described as the damage done by civilization to a normal physical act. Sometimes a man may ejaculate before he gets his penis into his partner's vagina, sometimes he may ejaculate the moment he penetrates her, sometimes he may simply be unable to delay ejaculating until she has reached orgasm.

Defining premature ejaculation is difficult. Some experts say that any ejaculation which happens before you both want it to happen is premature. Others argue that a man is a premature ejaculator if he cannot withold ejaculation long enough for his partner to have an orgasm five out of ten times they make love. A third group of experts say that a man is a premature ejaculator only if he cannot stop himself ejaculating for at least a minute after penetration. (If you think that is a short time then you should perhaps be aware that 12 per cent of men require no more than six movements of their penis to ejaculate, and cannot delay ejaculation for longer than six movements.)

Premature ejaculation occurs mainly in younger men. It tends to disappear after the age of thirty when the reflexes become duller. It is more common among men who don't have sex very often and paradoxically in men who masturbate a good deal. It is said that a meat diet tends to increase a man's chances of becoming a premature ejaculator whereas a vegetarian diet makes it unlikely. The problem is also said to be common among male horse riders and motorcyclists. Premature ejaculation is so common that at least one half of all men ejaculate too quickly the first time they make love to an attractive new partner. (But later the same night things are usually much better.)

Premature ejaculation is primarily a psychological problem commonly caused by anxiety, enthusiasm or excitement. Many men having intercourse for the first time with a new partner will lose control and ejaculate very quickly. Over-eagerness is a common cause. Anxiety about the problem will usually make it worse.

Now for some facts about premature ejaculation that every sufferer should know:

1. Men sometimes ejaculate prematurely if they feel that their

partner regards sex as an imposition

2. Sometimes men whose partners have just given birth will ejaculate prematurely. They feel bad about having sex with a woman who is a mother and so, driven by a subconscious force, try to get it over with as quickly as possible

3. Some women think that if their partner ejaculates prematurely he must be over-excited by thinking about another woman. This is extremely unlikely

4. Men who were starved of affection when young are often premature ejaculators

5. Many thousands of years ago, when man was just learning to stand, premature ejaculation was an asset. In the days when men were threatened by wild animals such as sabre-toothed tigers a man needed to get sex over as quickly as possible. An interruption didn't mean that one of the children wanted a drink of water, it often meant a life-threatening danger. A man who didn't ejaculate quickly didn't father many children and didn't live long

6. Many men who worry that they are ejaculating prematurely last between one and six minutes after penetration. That is within normal limits. Occasionally a man will be able to last for ten minutes or more – but this is rare. (Male chimpanzees routinely come in thirty seconds; their partners find satisfaction by having as many males as possible or necessary in close succession)

7. Some men believe that if they could keep going for longer their partner would be able to have an orgasm. They worry that because she doesn't have an orgasm every time it is their fault. The fact is, however, that many women who do reach orgasm directly and solely through intercourse need at least ten minutes of solid, hard thrusting. That sort of requirement can make sex far too much like hard work for many men. It is probably far better for both partners if he helps her reach orgasm by manual or oral clitoral stimulation or if she assists herself by masturbation.

And now for some techniques with which premature ejaculation can be conquered:

1. Having a second erection within an hour or so of the first is an excellent and simple way of dealing with the problem.

The second erection rarely disappears quite as quickly as the first

2. Try wearing a condom during intercourse. The sheath will reduce the stimulation likely to produce ejaculation

3. Try using a local anaesthetic cream (available from a pharmacy). This will have the same effect as a condom

4. You may be able to extend the lifespan of an erection by distracting yourself and concentrating on some unstimulating thought – a mathematical problem or some practical difficulty around the house

5. Satisfy your partner before you enter her. Knowing that she will not be left frustrated will reduce the pressure on you and probably enable you to last far longer

6. Tense your buttock muscles while you make love. This will help delay the moment of ejaculation

7. Prior to ejaculation your testicles will gently rise to the base of your penis. By gently pulling your testicles down before penetration and during intercourse you may be able to delay the moment of ejaculation

8. As teenagers many men learn to come quickly – either in school 'competitions' or because they are frightened of being discovered. Try to overcome this 'training' by masturbating and then trying to delay your orgasm as long as possible

9. Recruit your partner's help. She should sit on the bed with her back resting against the bed-head. You lie near to her so that she can hold your penis in her hand. She then masturbates you. The moment you feel that you are about to start to ejaculate you should tell her. She should then gently squeeze your penis at the point where the glans meet the shaft. She should hold it still for five seconds. This should arrest your ejaculation. You should then both relax for a minute before she resumes stimulating you. Using this technique you should be able to gradually build up your resistance, and your confidence in your resistance. Your partner can use a lubricant on her hand to simulate conditions inside her vagina.

Once you're satisfied that you are making good progress with this technique, begin practising inside your partner's vagina. She should sit on top of you and you should keep still. She then moves, slowly and carefully at first. You must tell her if you feel that you are close to coming – she should then stop for a few moments. After practising this technique as often as you can you should notice a considerable improvement.

Retarded ejaculation

This position is the opposite to, and far less common than, premature ejaculation.

Men may have difficulty in ejaculating – despite the fact that they have good erections – for several reasons:

1. They may have drunk too much alcohol or they may have taken pills which dull the reflexes
2. Sometimes men who have deliberately tried to hold back (either as a contraceptive technique or in the hope that their partners will reach orgasm) may find it difficult to come when they want to
3. Men may suffer from retarded ejaculation if they feel guilty about coming inside their partner for some reason or worried about making her pregnant.

If you suffer from retarded ejaculation you may be able to help yourself come by fantasizing. Alternatively, masturbate close to ejaculation and then replace your penis inside her. She may be able to help you reach orgasm by changing position or by using a different technique, for example fellatio or masturbation.

Priapism

Priapism was a Roman god who had a large, stiff wooden penis. Priapism is a condition in which a man has an erection he doesn't want and can't get rid of – there is no sexual pleasure or excitement accompanying it. Erections of this type sometimes occur during the night or may develop after taking a drug. If you suffer from this then I suggest that you visit your doctor for advice.

Female Sexual Problems

Most of the sexual problems that affect women are caused either by hormonal changes or by infection. Like men, however, women are also vulnerable to psychological forces and some problems are created by anxiety or apprehension.

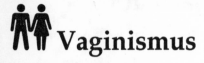 Vaginismus

Normally the vagina is a very flexible tube; however narrow it may seem to be it can expand to accommodate even the thickest penis. But sometimes the vagina does not expand; the vaginal muscles remain tightly contracted and attempts at penetration are simply painful. This condition is known as vaginismus and is regarded as the female equivalent of impotence.

Most women who have never had sex before are nervous. They look at the penis in front of them and wonder how on earth it is going to fit inside them. They may expect sex to be painful – either because of something they've read or because of something they've been told – and so they tighten up. When their partner tries to enter them they feel some initial discomfort and tighten up even more. The anxiety then creates more pain and the pain reinforces the anxiety. Vaginal muscle spasms keep the penis out.

Sometimes this fear of pain may be reinforced or supplemented by a feeling that sex is wrong or revolting. Cultural and religious pressures may conspire to make a woman feel that what she is doing is 'dirty'.

Occasionally, vaginismus affects women who are not virgins. When this happens there can be several reasons. First, there are physical causes. There may be pain caused by an infection. Hormonal changes, such as those which take place during the menopause, may mean that the vagina is too dry. A scar may have developed after a woman has had a baby or the doctor who has delivered the baby may have sewn up a vaginal tear so tightly that there genuinely is insufficient room for the penis to enter. Secondly, there may be psychological causes. A woman who is having sex with a new lover may feel guilty. If she is married and is beginning an affair subconscious forces may

conspire to make things difficult for her. It is not uncommon for a woman to suffer from vaginismus when she is with one partner but to be quite relaxed, capacious and comfortable with another.

If you suffer from vaginismus then there are two things you should do in order to rebuild your confidence and conquer your problem – assuming your doctor has confirmed there is no physical cause.

First, you should take the pressure off yourself. You and your partner should agree not to try to make love for six weeks. You should cuddle one another, touch one another and get used to one another's bodies. Touch his penis and gradually get used to it. Don't push yourself; take things at your own pace. Mutual masturbation is an excellent way to help relieve some of your fears and anxieties.

Second, you should gradually get used to the idea of having something inside your vagina. Find some time to yourself, make sure that your bedroom is warm and that you are not going to be disturbed. Undress and lie down flat on your back on your bed. Raise your knees up into the air so that your feet are flat on the bedclothes. Now wet the tip of your finger with saliva. Then gently, very gently, push the tip of your finger in between your *labia* and into your vagina. Be very gentle and remember that there is no hurry. If it hurts too much then stop. But don't give up just because it is a little uncomfortable. Stop for the moment when you're convinced that you aren't going to be able to get your finger any further inside.

Continue this exercise a couple of times every day. Each time try to push your finger a little further inside you. Remember to wet it before each attempt. If you like you can try using some baby oil or a lubricant of some kind.

Once you are content that you can get a finger inside you, then try with a tampon. Take it out of its cardboard applicator and smear the end with oil. Then slowly push the tampon into your vagina in exactly the same way that you pushed your finger inside.

When you can do this, try tightening your vaginal muscles as much as you can before you push the tampon inside yourself. Really get your vaginal muscles tight. Then put the tampon right up against the entrance to your vagina. You will almost certainly find you won't be able to get the tampon, or even a finger, inside yourself.

So now, deliberately relax your muscles. And as you do so bear down as though you were trying to push something out of your vagina. This movement will help to relax and open up your vaginal muscles. While you are doing this gradually push the tampon into yourself. It may be slightly uncomfortable to begin with but again, try not to stop unless it is painful.

At this stage most experts recommend that you start using proper dilators. These are usually made of glass and they look rather like graduated test tubes. Some are quite thin and some are quite thick. You should be able to borrow a set through your own doctor or through a gynaecologist, or you may be able to buy a set from a medical supplier. You use the dilators in exactly the same way that you have used the tampon starting, of course, with the thinnest dilator and gradually working your way up to the biggest.

If you can't get hold of a set of graduated dilators there are other things you can use, including your fingers. Once you can get one finger inside your vagina try using two. When you can get two fingers inside without any pain or discomfort try using three.

If at this stage you are beginning to feel more confident both in yourself and your relationship with your partner you can ask him to help you. Instead of using your fingers use his. You can still control them; you can still decide when the fingers go in and when they come out again.

You may find it helps if you put a pillow under your bottom to improve the angle at which entry is made. Or you may find it more comfortable if you lie towards the edge of the bed with your legs dangling and your feet flat on the floor. Your partner can then kneel down in front of you. Do remember that lubrication is very important and that, if you haven't got anything else, saliva is both safe and effective. Maybe he could prepare your vagina by applying the saliva directly from his mouth.

Once the six-week period is over, and as long as you are happy that your vagina can now accommodate at least two fingers at the same time, you can consider trying intercourse again. If you think you need longer then wait – don't rush things. Try to get yourself as relaxed as you possibly can, make sure that the bedroom is warm and use plenty of lubricant. If sex is impossible, don't worry. You simply need more practise and preparation.

Menopause

The majority of women reach the menopause – the 'change of life' – somewhere between the ages of forty and fifty-five. The production of sex hormones slows down, the ovaries stop producing eggs and monthly periods become irregular and eventually stop altogether. After she has gone through the menopause a woman can no longer get pregnant.

There are a number of problems associated with the menopause. Those most commonly reported include hot flushes and sweats; anxiety, depression, irritability and tiredness; an inability to get to sleep at night; dry skin and thinning hair. But in addition to these general problems many women also report some sexual difficulties. Some claim that their interest in sex has fallen, others say that because their vaginas are dry sex is too painful.

The fall-off in sexual interest is sometimes associated with the fall in the quantity of circulating hormones. But it is also commonly a result of the fact that when they reach the menopause many women stop thinking of themselves as feminine and attractive; they begin to think of themselves as old and assume that good sex must now be nothing more than a memory. None of this is true, of course, and there are thousands of women who regard the menopause as a new beginning. For the first time in their lives they realize that they can have sex without having to worry about contraception; they are freed from the risk of pregnancy. In fact, many women in their late forties and their fifties are more sexually active than at any previous time in their lives.

It is also important to remember that, as I have already pointed out, any individual will have less interest in sex if she (or he) has sex less often. If you haven't driven a car for a year you probably won't think about driving very often, and if you do find yourself behind a steering wheel you'll probably feel a little anxious and uncertain about your skills.

The main physical problem associated with the menopause is a dry vagina. This can be overcome by using an oil or jelly. You can either buy special products from your local pharmacy or you can use an unscented body oil or baby oil. Avoid anything that is too thick and greasy and any lubricants containing alcohol or drugs. Remember that saliva works well as a lubricant.

If your problems persist then it is well worth visiting your doctor. Hormone replacement therapy is safe and effective for most women who have sexual problems during the menopause. Women who have taken hormones during and immediately after the menopause report that their vaginas remained soft and moist.

👫 Cystitis and 'honeymoon cystitis'

Cystitis – an inflammation of the bladder – is one of the most common problems to affect women. Men can, and do, suffer from cystitis but women are far more vulnerable. The female urethra (the tube that carries urine from the bladder to the outside world) is very short and as a result infections can easily reach the bladder.

The two most common symptoms associated with cystitis are pain on passing urine and having to pass small amounts of urine quite frequently. Other common symptoms include the passing of cloudy or blood-stained urine.

There is a strong link between cystitis and sex, and 'honeymoon cystitis' is the rather delicate phrase used to describe cystitis associated with intercourse. Brides are supposed to be particularly vulnerable since they are likely to have sex rather more often than women who have been married a while, but 'honeymoon cystitis' certainly isn't confined to brides.

Sex can cause bladder problems in two ways: sometimes, when intercourse is perhaps too energetic, the female urethra, which runs very close to the vagina, is subjected to a physical battering; and sometimes an infection is simply passed on during intercourse.

The problem can be avoided, or at least minimized, by experimenting with different positions, by avoiding aggressive thrusting and by taking care with personal hygiene. Both partners should wash themselves before sex and women should empty their bladders after sex to make sure that any bacteria around the entrance to the urethra are washed away.

The problem of battering the urethra can sometimes also be minimized by placing a pillow beneath the female partner's buttocks when the missionary position is being used. And it's possible to help prevent infection being passed on by lubricating the vagina before intercourse.

 # Thrush

Also known as candida or vulvo-vaginitis, thrush is an extremely common infection. Thick white patches appear around the vulva and itching, soreness and pain on intercourse are common complaints. The bug that causes thrush can be transmitted sexually but thrush is not exclusively a sexually transmitted disease. The bug lives on the skin of most women and the symptoms can develop in a virgin or a woman who hasn't had sex for a long period.

The chances of a candida infection developing are increased when the naturally rather warm and moist area around and within the vulva becomes warmer and even more moist. Wearing nylon panties, tights or close-fitting trousers or jeans all make the development of thrush more likely. The changes in circulating oestrogens that happen during pregnancy or when a woman takes the contraceptive pill can also encourage thrush to develop. Taking antibiotics upsets the natural balance of bugs and makes thrush more likely, eating too much sugar makes the environment better for the bugs, and scratches and skin abrasions can increase the chances of thrush developing. Obesity makes candida more likely because the fatty folds around the groin keep the vulva unusually moist and warm. Inserting a tampon with dirty hands is another likely cause of infection.

There are lots of things you can do to reduce your chances of contracting thrush. Good local hygiene is important but it isn't necessary to use antiseptics or deodorants; indeed such products could increase your problems by irritating the area. Skirts, stockings and cotton panties or no panties are much better than nylon underwear, tights and jeans.

Once a candida infection develops, often signalled by a white, itchy discharge, there are several things you can do. To start with, do visit your doctor, he may prescribe an antifungal cream or pessaries. He may also want your partner to have a course of treatment since the infection can be passed between the two of you during sex. Some women have reported a reduction in symptoms after dipping tampons in plain yoghurt and inserting them. Yoghurt contains the lactobacilli bacteria which compete with and often oust the infection.

 **Trichomonas**

Since it produces a nasty vaginal discharge, trichomonas is sometimes confused with thrush. The difference is that the discharge associated with trichomonas is usually yellowish green and invariably smells. There is usually some redness and soreness around the vagina too. Trichomonas, like thrush, makes sexual intercourse extremely sore and uncomfortable. Although trichomonas is commonly transmitted through sex it can be picked up from infected towels and lavatory seats. If you think you could have this – or any other – vaginal infection, see your doctor for the appropriate treatment.

Dry vagina

Among pre-menopausal women at least one in five complain that they suffer from a dry vagina at least part of the time, and, as we have seen on page 145, during and after the menopause the problem is even more common. There are several possible causes, including fear, but often the woman concerned has not been properly aroused. A lengthier period of foreplay will frequently solve the problem, but lubricants are an even easier solution. A number of oils and jellies are available at local pharmacies, but saliva is the cheapest and most widely available lubricant.

Wet vagina

Occasionally women complain that they produce too much lubrication and that their vaginas are too moist. They say that the excess lubrication makes it difficult for either them or their partners to feel what is happening.

There is no cure for this problem I'm afraid. The only answer is to use a towel or some strong paper tissues to wipe away the excess.

Bleeding

You should always see your doctor for a check-up if you notice any bleeding after sex. There are several explanations. If you are a virgin and your hymen is still intact then there is almost bound to be a little bleeding. If your partner has been exceptionally rough then there may be some bleeding, particularly if your vagina was not given time to enlarge or to lubricate itself properly. In post-menopausal women the vagina's ability to lubricate itself diminishes considerably and bleeding may be a problem even if a woman is willing and ready. Finally, bleeding may occur after intercourse if the cervix is in any way damaged or inflamed.

Bleeding is not usually anything to worry about. But see your doctor and ask for his advice. He will probably want to examine you internally.

 Pain

Only a confirmed masochist enjoys sex which hurts – and there aren't many of them around. But there are numerous reasons why sex may hurt. Superficial pains and soreness can be caused by vaginal dryness, by allergy reactions, by cuts and sores or by localized infections. Forgotten tampons and other objects left inside the vagina can cause considerable discomfort and cystitis is another possible cause of pain. A rigid hymen, an opening made too small after the repair of a tear caused by childbirth, old scarring and vaginismus can also all cause problems.

Deeper pains can be caused by endometriosis, fibroids, chronic pelvic congestion (sometimes caused by having intercourse repeatedly without ever having an orgasm), ovarian cysts, a retroverted uterus, a prolapse and infection of the cervix.

Whenever sex is accompanied by pain a doctor's diagnosis should be sought.

 Incontinence

Men cannot usually pass urine while they have got an erection but women quite often lose a little urine when they are sexually excited. This is nothing at all to worry about. The few drops of urine that are released may, indeed, make sex more pleasurable by increasing the lubrication of the vulva and vagina. Even if accidentally swallowed – during cunnilungus, for example – small amounts of urine will do no harm (although swallowing a lot of urine regularly should be avoided as the unwanted electrolytes would probably put a strain on a man's kidneys).

👫 Inability to have an orgasm

There are a number of myths about the female orgasm. There are myths about vaginal and clitoral orgasms. There are myths about the intensity of the orgasm a woman can expect. But one myth causes more heartache than any other – this is the myth that every woman will be able to have an orgasm during intercourse. It is not true. The majority of women never do have an orgasm during intercourse. They only reach orgasm when they masturbate or when their partner augments intercourse with manual stimulation.

The fact that a woman doesn't have an orgasm every time she makes love, does not get multiple orgasms or does not want sex every day, does not mean that she is frigid or that there is anything wrong with her technique or with her partner's technique.

If you have difficulty in reaching orgasm here are some practical pieces of advice:

1. Tell your partner what you like and what turns you on. Try not to be shy about explaining exactly what you like. If you want him to move to one side a little then ask him. If you want him to kiss your breast then ask him. If you want him to suck your nipples, squeeze them, caress them or leave them alone then tell him. If you don't tell him what you want then he will probably never know
2. Try not to have sex when you are anxious and worried about everyday problems. Take the phone off the hook and ignore the doorbell if it rings. Try to relax and push your problems to one side (even if only temporarily) before you have sex. If you are preoccupied with mundane problems your chances of having an orgasm are low
3. Don't be afraid to fantasize. Read the chapter which starts on page 100. Most women find it easier to reach orgasm if they do fantasize. Most women who fantasize when they masturbate reach orgasm more readily than women who don't. Try reading books with sexy scenes or even watching sexy movies, then try to build what you've read or seen into your own fantasies. Don't be worried by your fantasies – there is a lot of difference between what happens in your

mind and what happens in reality

4. Be prepared to let yourself go. Many women dress up for
    sex (for example, in black stockings and suspenders) not just
    because it turns their partners on but because it turns them
    on too – both because they feel exceptionally feminine and
    because they like knowing that they are turning their part-
    ners on. You're more likely to enjoy sex and reach orgasm if
    you are prepared to enjoy yourself. Don't make the mistake
    of taking sex too seriously

5. If you have difficulty in reaching orgasm during sex, try
    masturbating to find out how you can best be turned on.
    Use your hands or try using a vibrator. Incorporate what
    you have learned into your love-making. Find the sexual
    patterns which are most likely to give you an orgasm.

👫 Lax vagina

When a woman has a baby her pelvic and vaginal muscles are
put under a considerable strain; they will have had to stretch to
allow the baby through. It is hardly surprising that they often
lose their tone and strength.

When this happens a woman will often complain either that
she no longer gets as much satisfaction from intercourse as she
got before or that her partner seems less well satisfied. This is
because the vaginal muscles no longer grip the penis tightly
when it enters; there is less stimulation for him and less likeli-
hood that her *labia minora* will pull down on her clitoris to make
intercourse enjoyable for her.

This problem isn't the disaster it may sound. By deliberately
exercising the relevant muscles it is possible to regain vaginal
muscle tone.

The muscles that control your vaginal walls also control the
flow of urine from your bladder and this link can be used to your
advantage. Begin your exercises by sitting on the lavatory with
your legs apart and your arms resting on your thighs. Then
force a little urine out of your bladder. Stop almost immediately,
as soon as the stream of urine has started. Use the muscles
around your vagina to stop the urine flow. For the next few
minutes continue to pass teaspoonfuls of urine in short bursts,
contracting your muscles to control the flow.

After practising like this for a while you should be able to contract and relax the relevant muscles without needing to control a flow of urine to prove the effect.

Now try exercising those same muscles while you are lying flat on your back on your bed. Undress first and make sure that the bedroom is warm and that you aren't going to be disturbed.

Moisten one finger and slip it gently into your vagina. If you have difficulty doing this, lift your knees up and put your feet flat on the bed. While the finger is inside you, try squeezing hard with the muscles around your vagina. You should be able to feel the muscles contract. Then let the muscles relax and go loose. If you repeat this exercise regularly you will be able to strengthen your vaginal muscles enormously.

Now, without putting a finger into your vagina, try bearing down, as though you are trying to push a baby out of your vagina. Then try moving the muscles the other way, so that if there was anything there it would be sucked up into your vagina. If you have something suitable – such as a vaginal dilator or a candle – to hand, you can exercise with that.

Once you've tried this exercise a few times you'll know how it feels. And once you've got the feel of it you'll be able to practise it whatever you are doing and wherever you are. You can try it in a supermarket queue or on the bus, while you're doing the washing-up or chatting to a friend.

Before long you'll have impressive vaginal muscle power – strong enough to squeeze anything that happens to be inside your vagina. I have little doubt that your sex partner will appreciate your new skill.

Pregnancy

Pregnancy can pose many problems both for women and for men, and yet most of those problems are based on myths and misunderstandings. The simple, basic truth about sex during a normal, healthy pregnancy is that if it's comfortable then it's almost certainly safe. Indeed, unless there are clear problems, there really isn't any reason why sex should not continue right up until the moment that labour itself starts.

There are some obvious restrictions. If a pregnant woman has had a previous miscarriage then she will be wise to avoid intercourse for the first fourteen weeks of her pregnancy. If she has had a number of miscarriages she may need to avoid sex for longer. And clearly any woman who is pregnant and bleeding should avoid sex. Finally, if the obstetrician looking after a woman advises her to avoid sex then she would be foolhardy to ignore his advice.

Many women find that their level of activity drops during pregnancy. There are several reasons for this:

1. Some worry about letting themselves go, suspecting that if they have an orgasm then they might go into labour. It is true that when a woman has an orgasm her womb will contract in much the same sort of way that it will contract during labour, but there isn't any evidence to suggest that this is likely to bring on an early birth

2. Sometimes, both parents avoid sex for fear of damaging the baby. A husband or lover may be frightened that he will hit the baby with his penis. This isn't very likely. The penis isn't big enough or strong enough to do any damage. Nor will semen do any harm. Semen does contain hormones called prostaglandins and these can cause uterine contractions, but the amount involved is very small

3. Pregnant women are occasionally embarrassed about their swollen breasts, enlarged nipples and swollen abdomen. They don't feel attractive and assume that their partner will not find them attractive. There are undoubtedly some men who find pregnant women sexually unappealing, but much more commonly, the opposite is the case

4. Some couples have less sex during pregnancy because one or the other partner finds it painful or uncomfortable. When

this happens there are usually simple solutions. Rear or side entry positions are often far more comfortable for both partners than missionary positions. He should thrust gently and be careful when touching her breasts since they are likely to be tender. If even these positions are too painful then there are no reasons why he and she shouldn't satisfy one another with oral sex or mutual masturbation

5. There is no doubt that some women lose interest in sex when they are pregnant for hormonal reasons. A woman's hormones change a lot when she is pregnant and her libido will inevitably go up and down too. A lot of women lose interest in sex for the first third of a pregnancy, have more interest than usual during the middle third and then lose interest again towards the end.

So much for sex *during* pregnancy. There are also many myths about when it's safe to start having sex after a baby has been born.

The truth is that it's all a matter of personal choice. Some couples want to have sex immediately afterwards. Some want to wait. Some women are too uncomfortable for several weeks, particularly if the birth has been difficult. Some men feel shy or embarrassed about making love to a woman whom they have seen give birth; they need a little time to adjust.

Just how sore sex will be for her depends on what went on in the delivery room. If the baby was born without a tear then there will be less discomfort than if a lot of stitches were necessary. On average the soreness after birth will last for about ten days but the pain, if any, will also depend on how gentle or rough he is.

Women commonly worry that they won't be attractive once they've had a child. They sometimes feel flabby and overweight. They suspect that they smell of babies, know that they have stretchmarks and worry about the fact that their breasts have got larger and possibly more pendulous.

Men can play an important part in helping women get through this difficult phase. A bunch of flowers, a bottle of perfume and maybe a little champagne will do wonders for a woman's ego.

Another problem is the fact that a young mother may be so wrapped up in her new baby that she hardly has time for her partner. He may feel left out of things. She may be too tired for sex after washing nappies and constantly feeding her baby. To overcome these hazards she must take care not to exclude him and he must make an effort to share the physical burden during the next few weeks, months and years.

I do not, by the way, feel that there is any need at all to worry about making love with a baby in the room. Your baby is far more likely to suffer if not making love results in a strain in your relationship.

Next, many women worry that after giving birth their vaginas will be too large. However, although the vaginal muscles do get very stretched during labour they shrink back to their normal size fairly quickly. And by doing simple exercises (described on page 152) it is possible to get the tone and power back into the muscles quite quickly.

Finally, if you have any other fears or anxieties, talk about them. He may get turned on by watching her breastfeed. He may prefer not to watch. She may not like him touching her breasts because they are too tender. She may find some positions uncomfortable. He may just want a cuddle. Unless you talk to one another you'll never know.

Old Age

So far in this book most of the advice I have given has been aimed at couples in normal, good health. But there are thousands of people whose sex lives are affected by age or infirmity. Men who have had a heart attack may wonder how safe they'll be if they try to have sex again and women with arthritis may find their customary position far too painful.

Sex is usually thought of as a young person's sport but men and women do not lose their sexual needs as they grow older. There are some physical changes but the sex drive doesn't just disappear at the age of fifty, sixty or seventy.

Here are some of the changes which take place as the years go by:

1. Men tend to have fewer erections and the ones they get aren't quite as hard as they were in their youth
2. Women's vaginas tend to be rather dry
3. Sexual needs and sexual desires don't disappear but they do diminish a little
4. It usually takes a man longer to get an erection when he is older. A stimulus which might have produced an instant erection forty years earlier will only produce an erection after a minute or two
5. Premature ejaculation is uncommon among older men. They are usually able to maintain an erection for much longer before ejaculation
6. His orgasm will probably be slightly less explosive. There will be less semen
7. After an orgasm it may be several hours before he can manage another erection
8. She takes longer to get aroused and her vagina takes minutes rather than seconds to start to get moist
9. Her vagina tends to expand less as she gets older; as a result it may be rather tighter. This probably won't be a problem unless she is also very dry, in which case artificial lubrication is the answer. However, at the same time, the vaginal walls become smoother and lose some grip
10. Her orgasm will be less dramatic. She may only have one contraction instead of a series of contractions.

None of these changes will make sex impossible or unenjoyable although together they may mean that it takes a little longer. Most people don't find this a problem.

Some old men worry that sex may endanger their health. There really isn't any evidence to support this fear. If sex was a major killer among old men then old men who didn't have sex (for example, monks) ought to live longer than old men who do. But they don't. The available figures show that monks and old men who abstain from sex do not live any longer than men who have active sex lives. To reduce the risks he should avoid having sex after a large meal or a hot bath (either can increase the demand on the heart by as much as 20 per cent) and should remember that illicit sex with a mistress is far more dangerous than sex with a regular partner because of the associated anxiety and guilt.

Two things are worth remembering. First, your brain will stay lively and alert as long as you use it and your body – and sexual skills – will remain active as long as you keep enjoying sex. Second, having sex won't stop you getting old but it will help you to feel younger and look younger than you are.

Illness

After a heart attack, an important operation or a period spent in hospital or convalescing for any other reason, most people gradually get back to work and/or the home and manage to resume a normal life. Sex is the one area that often presents difficulties. Men or women worried about making their condition worse – or of dying – may be reluctant to resume normal activities.

However, the fears are usually unfounded. Unless a doctor has specifically forbidden sex, or having sex is painful, there isn't usually any reason why it should be avoided.

On the contrary a healthy sex life is an excellent way to obtain essential exercise and a good way to relax. With a little care and a little planning sex is unlikely to hurt and very unlikely to kill. If you can walk up two flights of stairs, you can have sex.

Whatever the health problem may have been there are a few basic rules which should be followed:

1. Don't do anything that is painful. If it hurts then stop
2. Take things gradually. Don't start off by doing handsprings off the wardrobe
3. Choose your positions carefully. The partner who has been ill should do least work to start with. If he's been ill then choose the woman on top position. If she's been ill try a rear entry position. If you've both been ill try a side by side position. And remember that masturbating and oral sex are excellent variations that are unlikely to leave either of you exhausted
4. Avoid alcohol and rich and heavy meals before sex
5. If you have weak or painful joints keep warm. Make sure that the room is warm and the bed is warm. A warm bath beforehand may help. Heat helps to make joints more mobile
6. Experiment to find the time of day when you feel best. Late morning and early afternoon may be better than late at night or early in the morning.

Chapter 7

Myths And Misunderstandings

During the last twenty years I have worked as a general practitioner, an agony uncle on television and a newspaper columnist. I've received thousands of letters from readers and viewers and answered thousands of questions asked by puzzled, worried and anxious patients.

For this chapter I've set down, in no particular order, the questions I'm most often asked about sex – together with my answers. I always find it surprising how much so-called 'information' about sex is based on myths and misunderstandings; I hope my answers will go some way towards clearing out the worst.

It is always painful when a girl loses her virginity?

No, though it's easy to understand how this myth came about. In young girls a thin piece of skin called the hymen protects the entrance to the vagina. If the hymen hasn't already disappeared then a woman's first experience of sexual intercourse may be painful. Today, however, most young girls have already lost their hymen, either through taking part in active sports or through using internal tampons during their menstrual periods. If a girl is properly aroused before penetration takes places then defloration should not be painful. The more experienced and skilled a girl's lover is the less likely she is to suffer pain when she loses her virginity.

How will I know if I have an orgasm?

You *may* have a mind-blowing, earth-shattering experience that threatens to blow off the top of your head. But you're more likely to get a pleasant physical sensation, a feeling of warmth and a bit of a 'buzz' around your genital area. Afterwards you'll probably feel rather relaxed and sleepy. Men don't usually have any difficulty in telling when they've come. Women who are expecting something out of this world may not realize that the rather nice feeling they get is an orgasm.

Do some women fake their orgasms? If so why?
Yes, women do sometimes fake orgasms. Usually it's because they are unable to have an orgasm and they don't want their partner to know. This may be because they don't want him to feel disappointed or inadequate. Or it may be because they don't want him to keep on trying for hours.

Is masturbation bad for your health?
No. Masturbation doesn't cause blindness, or even short-sightedness, hairy palms, madness or venereal diseases. It isn't a sign of immaturity. Learning how to masturbate successfully is more likely to solve sexual problems than cause them.

When do men and women reach their sexual peak?
Men reach their sexual peak in their late teens and early twenties. Women reach their sexual peak in their thirties when their desire for sex is also at its greatest. It is, therefore, far more sensible for women to have toy boys than for older men to run off with young girls.

Is there such a thing as a male menopause?
Maybe. Men don't have a hormonal change but they may undergo a period (usually in their forties) when they realize that their lives are running out, that they are wasting time and energy on things that don't matter and that they haven't got long to go. They may also worry about impotence and sexuality. All this can lead to a second adolescence, with infidelity a common consequence.

How long does it take most women to reach an orgasm?
If a woman is going to reach an orgasm through straight inter-course then ten minutes of foreplay followed by about five minutes of vigorous sex should be plenty long enough. Many women need manual stimulation in addition to vaginal penetra-

tion before they can have an orgasm. For them, eight hours of continuous sexual thrusting would not be enough to produce an orgasm!

Is it dangerous to have sex during menstruation?

No, assuming that she does not have any blood-borne infection and that her partner has no skin lesion on his penis. Sex during menstruation is regarded as unacceptable by some societies for cultural or religious reasons but there are no major health reasons why a couple should not have sex at this time. Remember, however, that tampons dry out the vagina and so additional lubrication may be needed. It is possible to have sex while a tampon is still inside but avoid deep penetration and *don't* forget the tampon is there afterwards. Interestingly, most women are at their randiest when they have a period.

Should underarm hair be removed?

It's purely a matter of personal taste. Some people find underarm hair (axillary hair) distasteful. Others find it sexually exciting. Talk to your partner.

Should pubic hair be removed?

Again it's a matter of personal taste. There are no hard and fast rules. Some women with a lot of pubic hair trim it so that they can wear bikinis and hot pants. Some people find a shaved pubic area sexually stimulating. Others are excited by lots of hair. People in hot climates sometimes remove pubic hair for reasons of hygiene. If you shave your pubic area and decide you don't like it bald then you'll have to put up with an uncomfortable few weeks while the hair grows back again. Most women compromise, trimming off excess hair but leaving a bush of hair covering their *mons veneris*. Some women who do shave claim that their skin becomes exquisitely tender to the touch of both penis and fingers. They also point out that they avoid the problem of hairs getting trapped by the penis and that their partners don't have to worry about finding hairs in their teeth after cunnilingus. It is relatively rare for men to shave off their pubic hair.

If you prolong intercourse for a long period of time can it damage your health?

Neither the penis nor the vagina are designed for long periods of use. Too much rubbing of the penis will eventually make it sore (some snakes have two penises designed to be alternated) and may cause a burning sensation when urine is passed. Prolonged intercourse may irritate the vaginal wall causing soreness and itching.

Is it true that men have to have an orgasm in order to enjoy sex?

No. Like women, men get a good deal of satisfaction out of touching, and being touched, holding and being held.

Do women ejaculate?

Some researchers have claimed that women do ejaculate during orgasm. Others argue that the fluid they lose is urine. There's no firm evidence either way.

Does the size of a man's penis affect his partner's chances of reaching an orgasm?

No. The vagina accommodates itself to the size of the penis within the first few thrusts, regardless of size. Anything of finger size or larger is big enough. Some women find a large penis visually stimulating (in the same way that some men are turned on by large breasts) but in practice the size of a man's penis is irrelevant.

Does the size of a woman's vagina affect her partner's chances of reaching an orgasm?

The size of her vagina has very little effect on either partner's satisfaction although, if the muscles around her vagina have become very weak, then there may be less stimulation. If he has a small penis and she has a relatively capacious vagina he should introduce himself into her after relatively little foreplay. If he has a large penis and she has a small vagina then he can help her by waiting until she is in an advanced state of sexual excitement.

Is it true that there are two types of orgasm – clitoral and vaginal?

Sigmund Freud argued that little girls discover that they can achieve orgasm by stimulating the clitoris and later find that they must transfer their sexual response from the clitoris to the vagina. He said that women who fail to do this become vaginally frigid even though they can stimulate themselves to orgasm. He was wrong. During intercourse the thrusting of the penis causes the *labia minora* to move and stimulate the clitoris. The clitoris can, therefore, participate in ordinary vaginal intercourse. There is only one type of orgasm and it doesn't matter what is stimulated – the clitoris, the vagina, the breast or the anus.

Can some women have multiple orgasms?

After men have ejaculated there is a period during which they cannot have an erection. This period may last for a few minutes or for over an hour. This doesn't happen to women. If properly stimulated a woman can have a whole series of orgasms, one after the other. The vibrator has revolutionized the female orgasm. The hand gets tired during manual stimulation but with a vibrator a woman can have up to fifty orgasms in one session, stopping only when she is totally exhausted. (This can, however, cause chronic congestion of the pelvis and make the clitoris permanently larger.)

How long should sex last?

How long is a good holiday? How long does a good meal last? If you're both panting for sexual release then good sex may last two minutes. If you've just met someone, the first time can last all night and all the next day.

My partner often laughs when we make love. Surely sex is something that should be taken seriously?

Not really. Sex should be fun, unless you're involved in the serious business of trying to 'make a baby', and even then it should be fun. Your partner isn't laughing at you, he or she is laughing because he or she is happy.

When things go wrong (he can't get it up, she gets cramp, they both fall off the bed) laughter can defuse a potentially embarrassing situation. Lots of the things people do during sex *are* funny.

What is a nymphomaniac?

Anyone who wants sex more often than you do. The strange thing is that even today it is culturally acceptable for a man to have sex with lots of girls but still considered rather bad form for a girl to have sex with lots of men. A promiscuous male is regarded as something of a stud. A promiscuous female is regarded as a tart and called a 'mattress' or 'bicycle'. Most men and women who have sex with a *lot* of partners are probably really looking for love, friendship and companionship more than physical satisfaction. They may be reluctant to put everything into a relationship because, despite their need for love, they are frightened of being hurt.

Since vibrators give women good orgasms and never get tired isn't there a risk that eventually women will stop needing men?

I don't think so. A vibrator can never give a woman a cuddle. Nor can it offer love and romance. Vibrators are good only for orgasms and orgasms – despite what you may have read – aren't everything. Besides, the batteries can run down.

Is it normal for one partner to have to help put the penis into the vagina, or should it find its own way there without any help?

It's normal for it to need a little help.

Why isn't anal sex dangerous? Isn't there a risk of infection?

There are more bacteria living in and around the average human mouth than there are living in and around the average human anus. But there *are* some dangers. See page 86.

Are hairy men sexier?

In a study of college students in Illinois, USA, both men and women said that they thought that hairy men were sexier. One scientist has described an experiment in which he spent weekdays on a remote desert island with no human company and weekends on the mainland. The scientist used an electric shaver and every day he weighed his beard shavings. He found that his beard growth was much heavier on Fridays, when he was getting sexually aroused thinking about Saturday. He concluded that the sexier a man is, the more hair he grows. Thousands of men, and women, would disagree.

What are wet dreams?

Wet dreams are known clinically as 'spontaneous emissions of semen'. They usually start in boys at about the age of fifteen. They are rare among adult men and rarer still among men who are regularly having sex. When semen comes out of the penis in a wet dream (usually under the influence of an erotic dream) it tends to dribble rather than spurt. The erection is incomplete and the insufficiently expanded urethra prevents sperm leaving with its normal force. The odd thing is that when he wakes up in the morning a man who has had a wet dream will often feel randier than ever. A wet dream seems to be more of a stimulus than a relief.

Is it true that boys can sometimes grow breasts?
It's very common among teenage boys. Gynaecomastia, as it's called, occurs in 64 per cent of adolescent boys. It usually starts at the age of fourteen and lasts for a year or two. The swelling is a normal part of growing up and disappears as gradually and mysteriously as it arrived. Occasionally, prescribed drugs can produce gynaecomastia in grown men.

At what age do girls reach puberty?
In most countries in the mid nineteenth century, menstruation started at the age of around sixteen. It was thirteen in 1950. It is now eleven or twelve. Today it is not uncommon for a girl to begin to show the signs of puberty (sprouting breasts, thighs that flare, strands of pubic hair and finally menstrual periods) at ten years of age. We can thank dramatic improvements in living conditions for all this. (Puberty can be considered a problem if it starts before the age of eight or after the age of sixteen.) All this means that today's girls of ten may have all the sexual knowledge of twenty-year-olds from the start of the century, and the way some of them display themselves – often quite provocatively – reflects this. Boys tend to reach puberty a couple of years later than girls.

Should a woman wash out her vagina after sex?
It won't make a lot difference to her chances of getting pregnant. The bidet is occasionally useful – for cleaning yourself after anal sex, for example, or for washing your feet – but vaginal douching upsets nature and does very little good. The vagina is well equipped for looking after itself. Douching is likely to push infections further up into the vagina. (It is, incidentally, possible to wash sperm up into the cervix rather than washing them out if you douche after sex in an attempt to prevent pregnancy.)

Is it true that you can tell how sexually aroused a woman is by how moist her vagina is?

Not really. It is true that a woman's vagina will begin to lubricate when she is sexually excited. But there are other possible causes of lubrication, including anxiety and nervousness.

Why aren't women turned on by sexually explicit books and films?

Many are, though they're more likely to be turned on by soft porn with a story than by crude, hard porn.

What is a bisexual?

Someone who can enjoy sex with members of either sex. Bisexuality can lead to some behaviour that may seem bizarre to heterosexuals. After a friend's wedding night I later discovered that one bisexual man had had sex five times with the bride, four times with the groom, twice with the best man and once with the maid of honour.

Is it true that women can sometimes become allergic to semen?

Yes. But thankfully it is very rare. When it happens one answer is to use a condom.

Why do women prefer making love in the dark?

Who said they did? Women vary, as do men. Some prefer making love with the light on. Some prefer having it off . . .

Do men ever fake orgasms?

Yes, occasionally. Men occasionally suffer from retarded ejaculation (see page 141) and fake an orgasm for the same reason that women fake orgasms (see page 150).

Can a penis ever get stuck in a vagina?

It depends on what you mean by 'stuck'. It's possible for vaginal muscles to go into spasm or for a vagina to contract before the penis shrinks, but these problems are short-lived. Those stories about men and women shuffling into the local hospital with a blanket wrapped round them are apocryphal.

Is it true that the physiology of a sneeze is the same as the physiology of an orgasm?

No. And I suggest you avoid the temptation to say 'God bless you' next time your partner climaxes.

What is the difference between a transvestite and a transexual?

A transvestite is someone who dresses in clothes usually considered more appropriate for members of the opposite sex. He (or, less commonly, she) isn't necessarily a homosexual. A transexual is a person who feels stuck in the wrong body; he (or she) wants to become a member of the opposite sex. Surgery can sometimes make this dream come true.

Is it true that if you don't have sex for a long while your sex drive will disappear?

Yes. Regular sexual activity keeps the level of testosterone up. If sexual activity decreases then testosterone production falls. If you don't use it you'll lose it. If you don't have a partner, you can get into training with regular bouts of masturbation. It will take a couple of months to recover a normal sex drive.

Is it true that men don't need foreplay?

No. Men need, and enjoy, foreplay just as much women. Many cases of impotence could be prevented by good foreplay. It helps build up a good, firm erection and prepare the penis for sex. The better the foreplay the better the sex and the better the orgasm.

Why do some people shout out during sex?

People who are very demonstrative often make loud sounds during sex. They may cry, groan, scream, sob, grunt, moan or whimper. Some people shout out fairly obvious things, like 'I'm coming'. Some say irrelevant things, like 'Don't stop'. Some yell out 'No' when they mean 'Don't stop'. Some blaspheme ('Oh, God'). Some shout the name of a previous lover (embarrassing and potentially expensive). People who make a noise find it difficult to stop but others may be embarrassed by the noise, particularly if the room has thin walls. As a general rule men and women who make a noise during sex reach an orgasm more quickly, but just because people are silent during sex doesn't mean they aren't enjoying themselves. Finally, remember that it's rude to speak with your mouth full.

Why do some people talk dirty during sex?

Some men and women find talking dirty very stimulating. Others are stimulated by phrases like 'I love you'. A few drift into baby talk.

My boyfriend always gets a rash on his penis after fellatio. Can you explain this?

He's probably allergic to your lipstick. Change your brand or try removing your lipstick before you get down to business.

How can you tell if a man or woman is having an affair?

Look and listen. They will sparkle. Their skin will glow. Their eyes will glisten. They will take more care of themselves, get their hair done more often, start using aftershave or perfume, and dress better.

My girlfriend is very beautiful but she still seems to lack confidence. Why is this?

All women need reassurance about their looks. Strangely, the more beautiful a woman is the more vulnerable she is and the more she needs reassurance.

Why do so many older women like younger men these days?

Younger men are more virile and often look more attractive. They tend to be lean rather than fat and pretty rather than wrinkly. Women like young men for the same reason that, for years, older men have chased after young girls. Today older women are taking advantage of changing fashions. Older women are often at their sexual peak long after older men have started on the downhill slide. And, before you ask, younger men like older women because they are more experienced, more skilled and less restrained.

Is it true that some women pass out during or immediately after sex?

Yes. It's called the 'little death'. It happens to women more than men but can affect men too. Some individuals have a sort of semi fit. Others just drift into unconsciousness. It can be rather scary for the partner staying awake. If you pass out it's good form to warn your partner beforehand, otherwise you may come to in an ambulance.

Why is the incidence of rape on the increase?

If it is, there may be a number of explanations. One of the commonest is probably the fact that during the last few decades women have gradually become far more sexually aggressive. By this I don't just mean that women are now taking the initiative and asking men out, but that a large number of women now wear clothes which are blatantly designed to arouse the male sexual response: see-through blouses with no bra, short pants or jeans so tight that nothing is left to the imagination, clothes that emphasize their breasts. They deliberately leave buttons unfastened. They wear make-up and jewellery designed to draw attention to their sexuality. As a result the men working or travelling around them are kept in a constant state of sexual excitement. Inevitably many men are psychologically unable to cope; they are fired up by this exposure but they have no outlet for their physical urges. They respond inappropriately and an outraged society punishes them.

Can a woman rape a man?

Technically, yes. But legally, the courts don't seem to take male rape very seriously if it's performed by a woman. The legal attitude seems to be, 'he should be so lucky'. Similarly, when mature women seduce under-age boys sentences passed are usually extremely light. The molestation of boys by women is not taken as seriously as the molestation of young girls by men.

Is a circumcised man likely to enjoy sex more than an uncircumcised one?

Before I answer this question a few words of explanation are probably a good idea. In male circumcision the foreskin which normally covers the glans of the penis is removed. Sometimes this is done for religious reasons (for example, Jewish boys are always circumcised) and sometimes as a routine procedure when doctors believe that it is more hygienic (in many American hospitals circumcision is routine after birth). It is certainly true that if a foreskin is too tight it can produce problems. It can hinder a normal erection while dead skin, dirt and stale fluids can collect underneath it and become infected. Today, just about half the male population is circumcised. If the foreskin cannot be pulled back then circumcision is probably necessary and inevitable, although it is sometimes possible to stretch the foreskin under an anaesthetic. As to whether or not circumcision is good or bad for a man's sex life, that is largely a matter of taste. One advantage of circumcision is that it makes the glans of the penis rather dry and less sensitive; this usually means that ejaculation is delayed a little during intercourse. As long as the organ is clean, women don't seem to mind either way. Some prefer one style, some prefer the other.

Is it true that women are sometimes circumcised?

Yes. It's done for religious or cultural reasons since, unlike male circumcision, there are no medical reasons for it. Back in the nineteenth century women were circumcised in an attempt to treat a wide range of disorders including epilepsy, hysteria, moist palms and a wide variety of sexual problems. The operation was done on seamstresses who operated treadle sewing machines and who found the sexual stimulation produced by their thighs rubbing together too much to bear. And it was done when doctors couldn't think of anything else to do.

The operation described as female circumcision may involve the removal of one or more of these: the clitoris, the clitoral hood, the *labia minora* and the *labia majora*. The consequences include bleeding, infection and a host of sexual problems. When female circumcision was first done in Arabia and Africa the aim was to reduce a woman's sex drive and stop her straying or masturbating. Today some feminists advocate an operation which frees the clitoris from its hood because they believe it improves the female orgasm.

Are there any advantages to having regular sex?

Yes. Regular sex will help keep your body's production of sex hormones at a high level. You will, therefore, remain sexy and look younger, more vigorous and more alert than if you do not have regular sex. Studies at the University of Pennsylvania School of Medicine and the Howell Chemical Senses Centre in Philadelphia, both in America, have shown that women who have heterosexual sex at least once a week are more likely to have normal menstrual cycles, fewer infertility problems and fewer troubles during the menopause than celibate women and women who have sex only sporadically. There is also evidence to suggest that regular sex will improve your skin and general appearance. When you make love your metabolic rate more than doubles, your heart rate doubles and you use every single muscle in your body. Sex therefore improves muscle tone. The muscles of your back and bottom are particularly likely to benefit. Sex is better for you than aerobics or jogging. In addition to all these physical benefits there are mental benefits too. Regular sex can help to relax, help to maintain a good emotional balance and help you avoid depression. If sex is part of a loving, warm, caring relationship these benefits are doubled.

What are the differences between 'lust', 'love' and 'infatuation'?

You're in lust when your feelings about someone are entirely physical. The stronger the physical attraction the greater the chances that it's lust. 'Love at first sight' is usually lust at first sight. Infatuation is an obsession with someone. You can be infatuated with someone you've never met. Love is more complicated than either lust or infatuation. Love is wanting to be with someone, share things and experiences with them, look after them, protect them and hold them. Love is affection and friendship more than sheer sex. You are in love when you suddenly realize that you are kissing your best friend.

Why are women often randy when its most inconvenient – during a period?

Most human emotions go in cycles and the sex drive is no exception. The few days before a period are, for over a third of all women, the sexiest time of the month, closely followed by the time during and immediately after a period.

Shouldn't a woman's nipples get erect when she is aroused?

Some do, some don't. Nipple erection is an entirely involuntary response. Small muscle fibres within the nipple contract when stimulated in certain ways (touch and cold are two common stimulants) and that makes the nipple stand up. But not all nipples do this. If your nipples are very small then they may not have the facility to become erect. And if they are very large then it may not be noticeable when they become erect. If you really want to find out what a nipple looks like when it is fully erect splash it with cold water or hold an ice cube on it for a second or two (only very briefly as ice can burn).

Chapter 8

 # How To Get Pregnant

Getting Pregnant

Infertility is the medical problem that most commonly takes young adults to the doctor. At least one in ten couples don't seem able to start the baby they both want. Sometimes expert help may be needed at an infertility clinic. But in this part of the chapter I'll explain the things you can do to help yourselves.

When things go right

Each month changing hormone levels trigger the release of an egg from the thousands stored in a healthy woman's two ovaries. The release of an egg is known as ovulation and this normally takes place in between two menstrual periods. Once an egg has been released it travels down one of the Fallopian tubes.

When a healthy male partner ejaculates, millions of tadpole-shaped sperm are fired into the vagina at tremendous speed. Each individual sperm carries half a blueprint for a baby. The other half of the blueprint is stored in the woman's egg. So, it takes only one sperm to do the job but sperm come in teams of around 200,000,000. Some of the 199,999,999 unlucky sperm are designed not to rush for the egg but to help the chosen one get to the right position on time. When one sperm is close to the egg some of the remainder will, for example, link together to form a barrier stopping more sperm rushing on and getting in the way. One group of scientists worked out that if unravelled one of these sperm barriers would be over 541 yards (500 metres) long.

Most of the sperm die in the vagina but after a struggle for a couple of hours a few million manage to get through the cervix and into the womb. Inside they swim on for another five or six hours. At the upper end of the womb the sperm have a choice of two tubes. If they swim along one they will find an egg. If they swim along the other they will find a slow death.

Inside the Fallopian tube the sperm have to swim against a current which will eventually help force the fertilized egg down into the womb. When the successful sperm finally struggles inside the waiting egg the remainder will die.

Overcoming infertility

There are at least forty possible causes of infertility. Among women the common problems are a failure of ovulation and a blockage of the Fallopian tubes. Among men the most common problems are a failure to produce sperm of good enough quality and a failure to produce sperm in sufficient numbers. Infertility is often a symptom or a consequence of some other disorder, rather than the result of a specific problem. For example, general disorders such as diabetes or thyroid problems can cause infertility; sexually transmitted diseases can result in later infertility and, very occasionally, a woman may develop anti-sperm antibodies. When a man doesn't produce enough sperm or produces sperm of inferior quality the basic cause may be an old infection or an accident. Mumps, for example, is a common cause of male sterility. When a woman fails to ovulate the cause may be general (such as a loss of weight) or specific (such as endometriosis).

Sometimes infertility may result from the fact that sperm haven't had a fair chance of meeting an egg. The couple who make love once a year are less likely to start a family quickly than the couple who make love every day of the month. If he is impotent or ejaculates prematurely then she isn't likely to get pregnant either.

Finally, there are still millions of men and women who have no idea how babies are made.

I once saw a police sergeant who couldn't understand why his wife didn't get pregnant. It turned out that for years he'd used her urethra instead of her vagina. I've met couples who thought that babies were made by depositing sperm in the woman's navel (one woman thought that putting sticking plaster over her navel would act as a contraceptive). I know a woman who made her husband take the contraceptive pill because they enjoyed oral sex (she pointed out that it is called the oral contraceptive) and I've met countless other couples whose knowledge and understanding of the facts of life is a tribute to centuries of cultural and religious repression.

I hope that the information and advice elsewhere in this book will ensure that this sort of ignorance is no longer a possible cause of infertility!

Here are some practical pieces of advice that should prove helpful:

1. You will only get pregnant if his sperm and her egg are both in the right place at the right time. Remember that:
   * the first day of a cycle begins on the first day that a menstrual bleed starts. A cycle ends on the day before the next bleed starts. Ovulation usually occurs twelve to sixteen days *before* a menstrual bleed starts
   * an egg can be fertilized between twelve and twenty-four hours after ovulation
   * his sperm can (in theory at least) fertilize her egg up to five days after ejaculation as long as her cervical mucus remains wet, stickly and in a 'fertile' condition. In practice, sperm usually have a shorter active life than this
2. Sperm are very susceptible to heat. To ensure that his sperm are kept in the best possible condition he should avoid wearing tight jeans or tight underpants, should keep out of very hot baths and saunas and should sit with his legs wide apart as often as possible
3. After sex she should stay in bed for half an hour, draw up her knees and put a pillow under her bottom. All these things help increase the chance of sperm getting into and through the cervix. The more sperm that get into the womb the greater the chance of a pregnancy ensuing
4. A change in a woman's exercise pattern can reduce her chances of getting pregnant. A woman who takes up jogging or aerobics may not ovulate regularly

5. Stress, worry and anxiety can result in a failure to ovulate and a reduction in the chances of getting pregnant. There is much evidence to show that a woman's ability to conceive depends upon her state of mind. In some primitive tribes it has been claimed that women do not conceive until they have been married and it has become socially acceptable for them to have babies. This rule seems to apply however many sexual partners a woman has and however long she has sex without any form of contraception. Even in our highly sophisticated world there are many women who claim that they have conceived very quickly after deciding that the time was right for them to have children. Hormonal changes are easily influenced by all sorts of psychological factors (for example, if a woman is worried about something her period may be late). If she suspects that fears or doubts are the cause of infertility then she should try to learn how to relax, build up her self-confidence and replace anxieties with firm hopes and plans for the future

6. If a woman's weight changes, either up or down, then that can reduce her chances of getting pregnant

7. Some experts claim that it is possible for a woman to decide when she is most likely to become pregnant by studying the consistency of her own cervical mucus. The type of mucus produced by the small glands in the cervix changes through-out the menstrual cycle. Immediately after the end of a menstrual bleed the amount of cervical mucus produced will probably be quite low, with the result that the area around and just inside the vagina will feel dry and may be sore during sex or when a tampon is used. (By absorbing all moisture the tampon will exacerbate this dryness.) Then a very sticky type of mucus will be produced. This type of mucus, which does not contain much moisture, tends to leave a light yellow stain on white underwear. Finally, closer to ovulation the cervical mucus will be creamier and whiter. It will feel much wetter and, as ovulation approaches, the mucus will become wetter and clearer. The amount produced will increase too. The mucus, which at this time of the cycle has the appearance and texture of raw egg white, can be stretched out between the fingers. Most women ovulate at the time when their mucus is at its wettest.

Chapter 9

How Not To Get Pregnant

Contraception

Contraceptives have been used since men and women first realized the consequences of making love. Coitus interruptus, needing no special skills or equipment, is probably the oldest form of birth control, and was widely practised by the Hebrews. Recognising the aesthetice disadvantages of this method, many women enthusiastically experimented with different forms of chemical contraception. Egyptian women were mixing honey and crocodile dung into contraceptive pessaries 4000 years ago. Arabian women made contraceptives from pomegranate pulps treated with alum and rocksalt, and the Greek author Aristotle described a chemical concoction consisting of cedar oil, frankincense and olive oil.

Astonishing though it may be, it is quite possible that any of these preparations might have had contraceptive value. All would have affected the acidity of the vagina, and sperm are very sensitive to changes of this nature.

The sheath is also a fairly well-established device, though its use does not seem to go back beyond the sixteenth century. At that time venereal disease was common and the sheath was used more as a protection against infection than as a contraceptive. Japanese men wore sheaths made of tortoiseshell, horn or leather but most European males favoured a moistened linen sheath. The tortoiseshell condom can't have been much fun for either party.

Diaphragms and caps have been used for years and Chinese

and Japanese women used to cover their cervices with discs of oiled tissue paper. Anal intercourse was favoured by some Greeks while others apparently experimented with intra-uterine devices.

One writer suggested that after intercourse women who didn't want to get pregnant should get up, sneeze, douche and then drink something cold before making violent bodily contortions designed to displace the sperm. A Persian writer suggested that in order to dislodge sperm any woman who didn't want to become a mother should take nine backward jumps before sitting on her toes and stroking her navel with her thumb.

Those who were failed by such precautions would often remedy the situation later. Both abortion and infanticide have been used for centuries to limit the size of families. There is evidence that infanticide was practised in Europe until the nineteenth century.

By the end of the nineteenth century the average man and woman wanted something more effective and acceptable than crocodile dung and doctors and scientists all over the world started inventing more acceptable products. The rubber condom, the Dutch Cap (a special device designed to cover the entrance to the cervix) and the diaphragm were all introduced in the last twenty years of the nineteenth century.

Today there's quite a choice of available contraceptives. Aesthetic questions have to be balanced against failure rates, and safety and effectiveness compared. The information which follows is designed to help you make up your mind what to use. Remember that the chances of a woman getting pregnant after one single isolated instance of intercourse are approximately one in five!

👫 The contraceptive pill

For the last twenty years doctors have been arguing about whether or not women who take the contraceptive pill are endangering their health. Most now agree that women are at risk. If you are over thirty-five, smoke heavily and have a strong history of heart disease then taking the contraceptive pill will be risky. If you're under thirty-five, don't smoke and don't have a family history to worry about then the risks will be far less than the risks to your health of being pregnant if you don't want to be or, indeed, the risks involved in crossing the road.

There are scores of different brands of contraceptive pill but only three main types of pill: the combined pill, the progestogen only pill and the triphasic pill.

The combined pill contains a mixture of oestrogen and progestogen and is by far the most widely prescribed of all pills. In recent years low-dose combined pills have been introduced which are much safer but just as effective as the older pills. If you've been taking a pill for years without having it changed it would be worth checking with your doctor to see if there is a lower-dose pill you could take.

It is the two hormones working together in the combined pill which produce the side effects and, since the many different types of pill available contain differing proportions of oestrogen and progestogen, the side effects vary from one pill to another. The most common side effects produced by the pill include acne, weight gain, headaches, sore and swollen breasts, swollen legs, vaginal discharge, nausea, depression and bleeding between periods.

In a very small number of women the contraceptive pill can cause severe illness, even death. You should stop your pill and see your doctor straight away if you notice any of these symptoms: severe pain or swelling in your calf, bad chest pains, stomach pains, breathlessness, fainting, fits, speech defects, an inability to see clearly, bleeding after intercourse or any other unexplained bleeding, any sudden numbing or weakness, jaundice, any generalized skin rash or headaches. Most of these symptoms will be harmless but do seek advice anyway.

If you're 'on the pill' then you should see your doctor at least once a year for a check-up. Most doctors like to see patients at six-monthly intervals. The check-up must include a blood pressure check. You can also help yourself by learning to examine your own breasts and by reporting any unusual bleeding, pain or discharge to your doctor straight away. Do remember that contraceptive pills don't always mix well with other pills. Some antibiotics, tranquillizers and pain killers can counteract the effects of the pill. Check with your doctor if you need to take any drug while you're on the pill.

If you want to get pregnant then I suggest that you stop your pill six months in advance to give your own hormones a chance to get back to normal. And don't breastfeed while taking the pill since the hormones could get through to your breast milk. Do remember that when you stop taking a contraceptive pill your periods may be erratic for a month or two.

The triphasic pill which is said to have fewer side effects contains variable doses of oestrogen and progestogen. It seems safe and effective but it isn't yet as widely available or as well tried as the combined pill. The progestogen only pill (also known as the 'mini pill') is slightly safer than the combined pill but is not as effective. It is usually taken without a break and must be taken at the same time each day. Because it contains no oestrogen it is safer than the combined pill for older women and women who smoke.

Whichever pill you take do read the instructions carefully. If you are in any doubt ask your doctor for advice. The pill has been taken by millions of women around the world; it is one of the most efficient forms of contraception.

The rhythm method

For fertilization to take place the sperm and the egg must be in roughly the same place at roughly the same time. Since the woman's egg is released at ovulation, which normally takes place roughly midway between menstrual cycles, it is possible to estimate just when conception is most likely to take place. The same information naturally makes it possible to estimate when conception is least likely to take place. That's the principle behind the rhythm method.

An egg can live for about two days and sperm have a practical lifespan of a similar length. Theoretically, that means that if sperm can be kept out of the vagina for two days each side of ovulation then there is unlikely to be a pregnancy.

The difficult thing is deciding when ovulation will take place. It normally happens between twelve and sixteen days before the beginning of a menstrual period. So those who favour the rhythm method (it is accepted by the Catholic Church) suggest that sex be avoided between the tenth and twentieth days of the cycle, as long as the cycle is regular.

To give the rhythm method more of a scientific sound to it, some experts claim that you tell when ovulation takes place by measuring body temperature. The body temperature of a woman goes down slightly and then up slightly when an egg is released. So daily temperature readings will, in theory at least, help identify ovulation.

Another technique, the Billings method, depends on the fact that the mucus in the vagina becomes wetter and more transparent at this crucial time of the month.

This form of contraception really depends on ovulation occurring regularly. If it doesn't then there can be problems. Personally I think people who practise the rhythm method should spend at least one day a month knitting baby clothes and picking out furniture for the nursery.

 Spermicidal creams

Chemicals which kill sperm can be bought as creams, pessaries, tablets, foams and aerosols. They are both messy and ineffective. It's difficult to think of any advantages although they may be useful applied in conjunction with condoms. By themselves spermicidal creams are only suitable for experienced gamblers.

 Condoms

The condom, also known as the sheath, is the only mass-market contraceptive designed for use by men. The main disadvantage with the condom is that since it means pulling a thin layer of rubber over the penis it reduces sensation both for him and for her. Using a condom has been compared to playing the piano with gloves on or paddling with boots on. Despite this, condoms are very widely used. Around the world there are probably over 100 million people using them regularly and in some countries the condom is the leading form of contraception.

In an attempt to make their products more attractive, companies now make condoms in many different shapes and colours. You can buy products that are straight or contoured, transparent or coloured, thin or very thin and smooth or ribbed. You can buy them with or without lubricant added. You can buy a hypoallergenic sheath if your partner gets a rash when you use one. You can buy them with or without a teat on the end to catch the sperm. The only thing you can't do is buy different sizes – partly, I suspect, because the manufacturers are well aware that they would never sell anything less than a 'king size' and partly because condoms stretch so much that you can blow them up like a balloon. Well-made condoms are pretty tough though it's worth remembering that they can be torn by fingernails or teeth.

Condoms have a number of advantages: they're useful for unexpected, unplanned moments; they provide good protection against sexually transmitted diseases; they are convenient, can be bought by members of both sexes, in a wide variety of stores or obtained by mail order; can help delay orgasm when he suffers from premature ejaculation; are relatively inexpensive and don't produce any side effects.

A condom will only work at its best if it is used properly. It should be put onto the penis as soon as the penis becomes erect (some couples make this part of their foreplay, with her dressing the penis while he watches) and removed after ejaculation and before the penis becomes limp again. Artificial lubricants shouldn't be used with a condom since they may weaken the material. If she has particularly powerful vaginal muscles she should be careful (particularly in the woman on top positions) or she may succeed in sucking the condom off his penis.

Used properly the pregnancy risks are slight if you use a condom. If a hundred women rely on condoms for a year then no more than one or two will get pregnant – that's a failure rate comparable with some types of pill, the intra-uterine contraceptive device and other forms of barrier protection such as the cap and the diaphragm. When it does occur failure is usually due to over-eagerness, carelessness or tears produced by sharp fingernails or teeth. Condoms are particularly suitable for people whose love lives are unplanned or who have more than one regular partner.

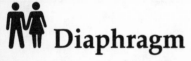 Cervical cap

This looks a bit like a large thimble and it fits over the cervix to prevent sperm passing out of the vagina into the womb. It's a simple and remarkably effective form of barrier contraception and in commemoration of its inventor, a physcian from Holland called Dr Aletta Jacobs, it is sometimes known as the Dutch Cap. If put into position before sex, a cap has the same low-ish failure rate as the condom.

The main advantage of the cap over the condom is that it doesn't interfere with anyone's pleasure. The main disadvantage is that it doesn't provide any useful protection against infection.

Women who use cervical caps don't usually take long to learn how to pop them into position. Some women find the cap a boon during menstruation. If the cap is put into position during an inconvenient period the flow of blood can be temporarily halted. When the cap is subsequently removed the blood will then be released.

Two of the things women don't like about the cap are that it's rather messy to put in, and it's easy to forget in the excitement of seduction and foreplay. Having to rush off to the bathroom to fit your cap can put a damper on proceedings. But one doctor at least is now making custom-built cervical caps which contain a small one-way valve. The valve allows menstrual fluid out but doesn't allow sperm in. It's claimed that this sort of cap can be left in position for a year at a time.

Diaphragm

The diaphragm is a soft rubber disc fitted with a metal spring. Like the cap the diaphragm acts as a physical barrier, preventing sperm from getting into the womb. Again, like the cap, the diaphragm needs to be put into position before sex and left there afterwards. The disadvantages are that the diaphragm is messy to insert and easily forgotten. It provides no real protection against infection. It's about as safe as the condom and the cap.

👫 Intra-uterine contraceptive device (IUCD)

The IUCD, which consists of a small piece of curved metal or plastic which somehow prevents a woman getting pregnant when it's put into the womb, has had a bad press in recent years and seems to be going out of favour in some parts of the world. It can cause heavy bleeding, cramp-like pains and a discharge. Occasionally an IUCD may work its way through the wall of the womb and into the abdomen. It can sometimes produce severe pelvic infection. Sometimes it can, unknown to its owner, escape from the womb. And there are horror stories of babies being born triumphantly holding their mother's IUCD in their tiny fists.

On the other hand some women find IUCDs to be safe. effective, comfortable and convenient. They can be left in place for a year or so, they won't usually be displaced by menstrual bleeding, tampons or sex and they don't interfere with anyone's enjoyment. It's fairly easy to check that an IUCD is still in place by feeling for the thread that should poke out through the cervix. The IUCD is probably about as effective a form of contraception as the condom.

👫 Coitus interruptus

The theory behind coitus interruptus (which is also known as 'being careful', 'pulling out', 'being considerate', 'having self-control' and, more quaintly, 'getting off at the last but one stop') is that by taking his penis out of her vagina before he ejaculates a man can ensure that pregnancy is avoided.

First recommended by Hippocrates this technique costs nothing and is widely used. The snag is that apart from the fact that this form of so-called contraception isn't much fun for either party (both are watching to make sure that he doesn't make a mistake and so neither is likely to enjoy what's going on) it isn't very efficient. Just before ejaculation some sperm are quite likely to leak out of the penis and into the vagina without any warning. The result is an unexpected, and often unwanted, pregnancy. Many pregnancies among women over forty result from the use of the technique. She is too old for the pill and too embarrassed to go into the chemist and buy a packet of condoms. They both probably think she's no longer fertile.

A variation on this theme occurs when he presses on the base of his penis, compressing the urethra at the very moment of ejaculation. The pressure can force the semen to flow back up into the bladder rather than out of the penis. The snag is that if this technique is used a lot he may end up always ejaculating back up into his bladder and become infertile.

Sterilization

Sterilization operations can be performed on men or women.

When she decides to be sterilized the gynaecologist will make a small hole in her abdomen to reach her Fallopian tubes. The surgeon then either cuts or removes parts of both tubes and seals them with clips or using diathermy. The whole procedure takes no more than twenty minutes and usually involves one or perhaps two days in hospital.

This operation is usually effective and not easy to reverse. Because it does not involve the removal of any hormone producing organs it does not affect the woman's feelings or sex drive at all. If anything her sex life is likely to be improved because her fear of getting pregnant will have disappeared. (Since there is always a risk that an egg may be waiting in the womb it is wise to take additional precautions until after the next menstrual period.)

The operation on men, known as a vasectomy, is even simpler. Using a local anaesthetic the surgeon closes the tubes down which sperm travel from the testes to the penis. The operation takes about ten to twenty minutes. Afterwards, although there are no sperm in the semen, there is no visible difference. It usually takes ten or twenty ejaculations to clear the waiting sperm from the near side of the two tubes and men are advised to have two tests done to check that their semen no longer contains any sperm. It is sometimes possible to reverse the operation but it should be regarded as permanent.

After a vasectomy a man is infertile, but there will be no change in sex drive or in his ability to have an erection or to ejaculate.

👫 Morning-after pills

If you have sex without using any form of contraception it is possible to stop a pregnancy developing. This is known as bolting the stable door after the stallion has serviced the mare.

The pills you need can only be obtained from a doctor and they must be obtained as soon as possible (though there's no need to be quite so determined as the young couple who rang a doctor friend of mine at two in the morning to tell him they'd just made love without a condom and would he pop round with a prescription). You need to take the first two pills within, at most, seventy-two hours of making love and the second two tablets within another twelve hours. The pills work by preventing implantation should an egg have been fertilized. This method seems both safe and effective and has few side effects. The hormone doses are fairly low.

Morning-after pills can only be used up to seventy-two hours after sex but copper intra-uterine contraceptive devices, inserted up to five days after sex, also have a contraceptive effect after the event and these are clearly suitable for women who for some reason haven't been able to get to a doctor within the necessary period.

👫 The abortion pill

Every year around the world 150,000 women die as a result of surgical abortions. Many die after long and painful illnesses. There is now a new abortion pill available which should make surgical abortion a thing of the past. A woman needs to take just one pill and use one special pessary during the first six or seven weeks of an unwanted pregnancy to produce an abortion.

Chapter 10
Sexually Transmitted Diseases

For the last few years AIDS has swamped our view of sexually transmitted disease. In fact, as is now clear, AIDS is not a major threat to hetrosexuals but the other sexually transmitted diseases *are* a real problem. The incidence of sexually transmitted diseases has been rising steadily for the last few decades.

First, here are some general facts about sexually transmitted diseases (STDs):

1. STDs are among the most common diseases in the world
2. STDs can be caused by bacteria, parasites, yeasts, viruses, chlamydia, fungi and mites
3. The symptoms of STD infection include rashes, swellings, urinary symptoms (such as bleeding, frequency and pain), soreness, itching, discharges that have increased, changed or become smelly, lumps, ulcers and warts. Bleeding and pain are also symptoms to look out for. The three most important symptoms are sores, ulcers and a discharge
4. STDs are often passed on in 'surprise bundles' with partners handing over several different infections at once
5. Many sufferers don't have any symptoms at all
6. Reliable statistics are difficult to come by but the commonest STDs are probably candidiasis, trichomoniasis, non-specific urethritis, gonorrhoea, warts and herpes
7. Once an STD has been caught it must be diagnosed as quickly as possible. And that means a visit to a doctor, hospital or clininc. 'Alternative' medical practitioners cannot diagnose or treat STDs effectively
8. Apart from the pain and discomfort they cause it is

important to treat STDs quickly because they can cause
many damaging complications including pelvic infections
and inflammatory diseases. Women with STDs who get
pregnant can sometimes infect their babies too

9. Women seem more prone to suffering the serious problems
associated with STDs than men, perhaps because they are
less aware of the symptoms of potentially hazardous disease

10. Avoiding STDs is difficult as it isn't always easy to spot
sufferers. Even a close examination may fail to reveal
tell-tale signs – and how many people go on dates with a
magnifying glass at the ready? Barrier contraceptives such
as condoms (and to a lesser extent caps and diaphragms)
seem to provide some protection. And you may be able to
help yourself a little by passing urine after sex and by
washing with soap and water.

AIDS

The first cases of AIDS (acquired immune deficiency syndrome)
were reported in June 1981 in California. Since then AIDS has
become the subject of many misunderstandings. Some doctors
have wildly exaggerated the risk to heterosexuals and AIDS has
become the hoax of the century, the crisis that never was.

By the middle of the 1980s private screening clinics had
sprung up all over the place, some insurance companies had put
up their premiums by as much as 150 per cent and big
international drug companies were raking in huge profits
because of the scare. Shares in one drug company that produced
a new anti-AIDS drug rocketed by 360 per cent in just twelve
months.

Here are the facts all heterosexuals should know about the
disease:

1. The HIV virus that causes AIDS causes death and diseases by
damaging the human body's own defence systems. The
patient gradually becomes more and more susceptible to
infections and diseases

2. Patients who have AIDS only get symptoms from the diseases
they catch because of their vulnerability. In the early stages of
the disease the virus that causes AIDS causes no symptoms.

After a while the most common symptoms include shortness of breath, coughing, swollen glands, skin diseases, night sweats, bruising, sores, headaches, blurred vision, diarrhoea, loss of appetite, aching muscles and difficulty in swallowing. Patients with AIDS will usually have several of these symptoms for long periods of time. All of these symptoms can, of course, be caused by diseases other than AIDS

3. AIDS is not basically a sexually transmitted disease, it is a bloodborne disease. It gets into the bodies of drug addicts if they share needles. Many sufferers of AIDS are haemophiliacs who acquired the disease after being given infected blood. Homosexuals are prone to AIDS because they commonly have anal intercourse with one another and anal intercourse often causes bleeding

4. Anything which involves the spread of contaminated blood can spread the disease. So, for example, using unsterilized ear-piercing, acupuncture or tattoo needles can all spread AIDS

5. According to one of the biggest, most important, most prestigious investigations into any disease ever published – the European Study Group investigating AIDS in Europe – 'the only sexual practice that clearly increases the risk of male to female transmission of AIDS is anal intercourse. . . No other sexual practices have been associated with the risk of transmission'. Similarly, one of the earliest American studies showed several years ago that the only sexual practice which was found likely to lead to AIDS was receptive anal intercourse. If you practise straight sex (and especially if you avoid sex with drug addicts, prostitutes and bisexuals) you are as likely to be hit by lightning as you are to die of AIDS contracted through sex. These studies confirm numerous other studies which show that AIDS is not a disease which threatens heterosexuals in the way that it threatens homosexuals.

Others

Chlamydia

Known as the Cinderella of sexually transmitted diseases, Chlamydia is now the most common in the Western world. It is ten times as common as herpes and far more dangerous. In America it causes sterility in about 11,000 untreated women every year. It is a common cause of problems among new-born babies. And some experts think that it is involved in 50 per cent of all cases of pelvic inflammatory disease. Virtually unheard of just a few years ago, chlamydia is undoubtedly the disease of the 1990s.

The importance of chlamydia only became clear when researchers investigated the condition Non Specific Urethritis (also known as NSU and as Non Gonoccal Urethritis) and found that in about 50 per cent of cases the organism causing the disease was chlamydia. It was also shown that the sister disease, Non Specific Genital Infection, was very likely to be caused by chlamydia too.

Men with chlamydia usually experience a burning sensation when they pass urine, and a discharge. And their illness is often diagnosed as gonorrhoea. In women the same mistake is often made, as the pain on passing urine and the vaginal discharge mimic gonorrhoea.

But when chlamydia is treated with penicillin (the drug normally prescribed for gonorrhoea) nothing happens. The drugs tetracycline or erythromycin are needed to conquer chlamydia.

Gonorrhoea

Gonorrhoea is still one of the most common of all STDs. Of the women who contract this disease, 60 per cent will have no symptoms at all. The rest usually notice fairly vague, non-specific symptoms such as a vaginal discharge and a burning on passing urine.

The symptoms of gonorrhoea usually develop within two to ten days after having sex with a carrier.

Diagnosing and treating gonorrhoea is extremely important. The infection can produce pelvic infections and every year many thousands of women become sterile because of the infection. If a woman with the disease gives birth her baby can contract a very unpleasant eye infection.

 Herpes

Here are the facts about this most worrying of diseases:

1. There are two types of herpes: herpes simplex 1 (HSV1) and herpes simplex 11 (HSV2). Both viruses can infect either the mouth or the genital area
2. Herpes can be transmitted sexually but also in other ways. The first symptoms of a herpes infection can appear up to thirty years after the virus arrived on the skin. An infected mother washing her child can give it herpes which only erupts half a lifetime later. The herpes virus HSV2 can live for seventy-two hours on towels, clothing and lavatory seats. (It can, however, be killed by bleach)
3. Herpes is increasing by about 12 per cent a year, ironically because of improving social conditions not increased sexual promiscuity. These days we rarely share baths and towels and so most of us grow up without being exposed to the herpes viruses. A generation or two ago people generally acquired immunity to herpes when exposed to the infection as children.
4. Severe recurrences of herpes are relatively rare. Between a third and a quarter of suffers have one attack and no more. Another third get occasional, infrequent, minor outbreaks. Only a third of herpes sufferers get troublesome recurrences. And even those are not usually as painful as primary attacks.
5. Herpes is not a new disease. The Roman emperor Tiberius tried to stamp it out by banning kissing. Shakespeare wrote about it in *Romeo and Juliet*
6. Doctors treat herpes with a prescription drug (acyclovir)
7. Herpes kills about one baby in every 250,000. Half the

babies who have herpes acquired their infection from their mothers, the other half from visitors or nurses. If a pregnant woman has active herpes then the danger can be avoided by delivering her baby by Caesarian section

8. There are many different strains of the herpes virus. It is possible to get infected with different types of virus

9. The symptoms of herpes appear gradually. A few days, perhaps a week, after sexual contact the sufferer will feel a little tired. He may have a fever and a headache, or backache and stiffness. As these general symptoms appear so more specific symptoms develop. There will be some local genital irritation and very probably a discharge; there may be pain or burning on passing urine. About four days after the onset of the irritation small blisters will probably appear on the penis or around the vagina; these may well be sore. Tender nodes will swell in the groins as well

10. If you have herpes you should follow these general rules: avoid having sex when a herpes lesion is visible; wash your hands carefully after visiting the toilet; remember that trauma can bring back symptoms so be gentle during sex until the vagina is well lubricated; remember a condom will provide some protection as will barrier creams; don't touch or kiss cold sores or genital sores; remember that stress can make herpes lesions worse

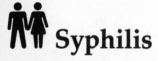 Trichomonas and thrush

Are dealt with on pages 147–148 since they are not only transmitted through sex.

Syphilis

Syphilis, first brought to Europe from America, used to be widely feared and extremely common. Today it is relatively rare.

It begins with a painless sore which looks like an ulcer and which appears on the penis or outside of the vagina. The patient will probably have a 'flu-like illness and swollen glands too. The first symptoms of syphilis can appear anything from nine to ninety days after sex with an infected partner.

If caught early syphilis can be treated effectively with antibiotics such as penicillin. Even if left untreated the symptoms disappear spontaneously after a few weeks or months. Sufferers stop being infectious about two years after first contracting the disease, although mothers can still pass the infection onto their babies after that.

But – and it's a big but – if syphilis goes untreated it can produce heart or brain disease twenty or thirty years later. It is, in many ways, one of the most horrifying of all the STDs.

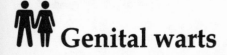 Genital warts

The incidence of genital warts is increasing. Like all warts these are caused by a virus. Transmitted by sexual contact they can be found on the penis, around the outside of the vagina and elsewhere in that immediate area. Sometimes there may be only one or two small warts visible but occasionally huge warty growths can develop.

Genital warts can be burnt off, frozen off, removed surgically or painted with caustic substances – all under medical supervision of course.

Index